*Teilhard de Chardin*

# Teilhard de Chardin

## The Man and his Theories

ABBÉ PAUL GRENET
*translated by*
R. A. RUDORFF

*Profiles in Science*

*Souvenir Press*

Edited by Jacques Ahrweiler

First British edition published 1965 by Souvenir Press Ltd.
34 Bloomsbury Street, London W.C.1
and simultaneously in Canada
by The Ryerson Press, Toronto 2, Canada

*Printed in Great Britain by*
*The Camelot Press Ltd., London and Southampton*

NIHIL OBSTAT

*Westmonasterii, 18th January 1965*
Joannes M. T. Barten, S.T.D., L.S.S.


IMPRIMATUR

*Westmonasterii, 18th January 1965*
Patritius Casey
Vic. Gen.

# Acknowledgements

---

Grateful thanks are due to M. Jean Piveteau, of the *Académie des Sciences, Professeur de Géologie en Sorgonne*, Reverend Father F. M. Bergounioux, O.F.M., Director of the Palaeontological Laboratory at the *Institut Catholique de Toulouse* and Reverend Father André Hayen, J. J., professor at the *Scolasticat* of Eegen-hoven-Louvain, for having suggested several corrections and improvements, and to Reverend Father General Fessard for lending several unpublished letters to the author.

I should also like to take the opportunity of thanking *Éditions Albin Michel, Éditions Bernard Grasset*, the Jesuit journal *Les Études*, the review *Les Études philosophiques*, and the *Librairie Plon* for permission to quote from various of Teilhard de Chardin's writings, and the Citroën company for providing me with photographs taken during the Yellow Expedition.

# Contents

# SELECTED WRITINGS

# Illustrations

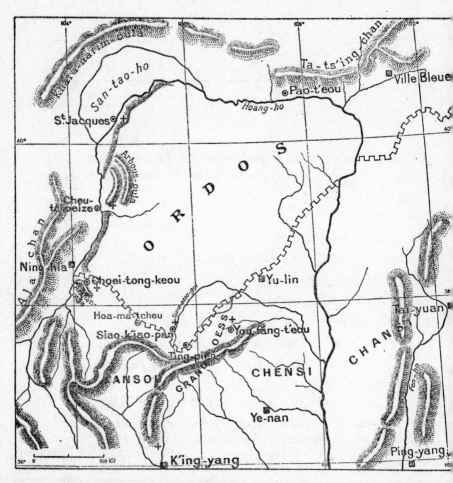

Map of palaeolithic deposits in the Ordos region. (*Courtesy of the Institut de Paléontologie humaine, Paris.*

# I

## *His Life*

MARIE-JOSEPH-PIERRE TEILHARD DE CHARDIN was born on May 1, 1881 at the château of Sarcenat, near Orcines, in the neighbourhood of Clermont-Ferrand, the fourth child of a family that was eventually to number eleven, after losing several children at an early age.

His mother Berthe-Adèle de Dampierre d'Hornoy (1853-1936) was of Picard stock and was a great-grand-niece of Voltaire. She had received the strict religious education of the time and was a shining example of inner piety, overflowing charity and complete humility.

A privileged witness of the family, Mlle Teilhard-Chardin, a cousin of Pierre Teilhard, has left the following account of the mother:

"The mother's influence on her children was far-reaching, and has left them with imperishable memories. The perfect dignity and modesty of this great lady who was able to control herself without ever raising her voice—although her soft voice could be irresistibly commanding—inspired them to veneration, and her clear-sighted goodness won their love and confidence. She made her children become men and women of honour and conscience, and—above all—Christians. Like Lamartine's mother, who

Explained to us the God that we felt in her

by some secret process of communication between her soul and
that of her children, Berthe Teilhard transmitted a sense of the
Divine Presence to her children, thus striking the first spark
that was to grow into a burning flame in Pierre's soul. When
Pierre learnt of the death of his 'dear saintly mother' during his
exile in the Far-East in 1936, he declared: 'It is to her that I
owe all that is best in myself.' "

The father, Alexandre-Victor-Emmanuel (1844-1932), was a
farmer by profession with a leaning towards natural history, a
man of humanist culture with a taste for palaeography.

He has been described by the same witness:

"My uncle Emmanuel was a very tall man with a noble
carriage, clear eyes and a moustache *à la gauloise*. His silences
intimidated his nephews, and, I think, his children as well.
The few words he spoke were unexpected, and pithy, being a
blend of humour and good cheer. He had been a pupil at the
Ecole de Chartes and put his erudition at the disposition of his
province, spending his life patiently sifting through the Archives
of Montferrand—an enormous labour of love which rescued
the annals of a whole past age in the history of Auvergne from
the dusty shelves of the archives. (It was Emmanuel Teilhard
who has the honour of discovering the only letter dictated by
Joan of Arc, bearing her signature (then unknown).) At the
same time he took a direct part in the administration of several
estates, as a real *gentleman-farmer** (I apologise for using an
English term for something so French, but my uncle would
forgive me, for he received many English journals dealing with
his favourite subjects such as agriculture, hunting, and horse-
racing). As a humanist who wished to maintain his culture he
read a great deal, especially history of course, and he showed
taste in the choice of his children's reading-matter. He supervised their Latin studies himself until they were old enough for
college. He also contributed to the formation of their character by giving them a taste for nature and by encouraging them
to make natural history collections of insects, birds and stones.
I was often surprised by the sight of my cousins running after
butterflies and lovingly raising frightful caterpillars which
turned into rare butterfly specimens which they then pinned
down in their glass cases. The young Pierre was fond of 'pebbles'

* In English in the original—Transl.

and I think we still have here* his earliest collection of minerals, which was the first modest step towards his scientific career as a geologist."

A month before his eleventh birthday, in April 1892, Pierre Teilhard de Chardin entered the Jesuit College of Notre-Dame-de-Mongré at Villefranche-sur-Saône, where he joined the fourth form.

At that time the teacher of the humanities was Henri Brémond, still a Jesuit then, and the teacher of physics—one of Pierre's favourite masters—was Father Desribes. Teilhard did consistently well in sciences and letters and took his *baccalauréat-és-lettres* without any difficulty, also being awarded the college prize of honour, among seven others, including a good conduct prize which he was voted by the pupils with the approval of the masters. His fellow-pupils also voted for him as secretary and then prefect of the Congregation of the Immaculate Conception.

When he left college he was thin and anaemic and needed a year of respite: his father made him use it to study elementary mathematics.

In 1898, at the age of eighteen and at the moment of leaving the Jesuit Fathers, his vocation had already revealed itself:

"At the age of seventeen," he declared, "the desire for utmost perfection determined my vocation as a Jesuit."†

On March 20, 1899, he became a novice at Aix-en-Provence, remaining there until the end of September in 1900.

In October 1900 he began his *juvenat*, i.e. the period of literary training made compulsory by the Order for its members. He took his first vows on March 25, 1901, and took his degree in letters in 1902 at the University of Caen.

1902 was the year in which the anti-clerical policies of Emile Combes triumphed in France. The laws of "exception" obliged the Jesuits to leave France for Jersey where the young Teilhard returned to the study of philosophy until 1905. At the same time he was regularly trained from 1904 onwards by Father Felix Pelletier in scientific surveys, resulting in a joint paper on the mineralogy and geology of Jersey.

The period September 1905 to September 1908 was spent by Teilhard as a teacher in a college, following the usual Jesuit

---

* At the château of Sarcenat.　　　　† Claude Cuénot, p. 18.

training schedule. He was sent to the College of the Holy Family at Cairo to teach chemistry and physics, but together with his colleague Father Joseph Clainpain, and their pupil Anastase Alfieri (since General Secretary of the Entomological Society of Egypt) he enthusiastically took part in expeditions which had little to do with either chemistry or physics. It was as a naturalist, a geologist and a palaeontologist that he explored Fayoum, the Mariut desert, Minieh and Mokattam as early as 1907. In 1908 he wrote a study of *The Eocene of the Minieh Region*.*

Pierre Teilhard spent his four years of theological study from 1908 to 1912 at Hastings—not without numerous forays into the spheres of natural history and geology, and always with the inseparable Father Felix Pelletier. A professor at Cambridge University noticed the two friends' studies in botany and palaeobotany, and drew them to the attention of the scientific world.† Claude Cuénot declares that at this time Pierre Teilhard had already gone beyond the "amateur" stage,‡ and that his interest in vertebrate palaeontology dates from that time.

On August 14, 1911, Pierre was ordained a priest in the presence of his parents, who received Holy Communion from his own hands the next day.

It is in these years of theological study during which his studies in natural history were far from being neglected, that Teilhard de Chardin wrote his first works, with the permission of his superiors. In them, scientific research was indissolubly allied to religious conviction: Teilhard examined religious facts scientifically, and tried to understand scientific phenomena in a religious spirit as may be seen by reading his article "The Miracles of Lourdes and Canonical Investigations" in *Études* (January 20, 1909), the article "Man" in *Apologetic Dictionary of the Catholic Faith*, "Man and His Relation to Church Teachings and Spiritualist Philosophy" (first written in 1909 but not published until 1912) in *Le Correspondant*, November 10, 1912; *Establishing the Features of a Disappearing World*; the *Religious Ethnological Week at Louvain*; and lastly, "Prehistory and Its Progress" in *Études* (January 5, 1913).

* Published in 1909 by the *Bulletin de l'Institut égyptien*, Alexandria.
† In the *Quarterly Journal of the Geological Society of London*, 1913.
‡ Although an article in *Études* (July-August 1950) on Teilhard declared that "There was nothing to suggest that the young geologist would ever go beyond the amateur stage."

But before he could follow this double path which was essentially one, he needed specialised scientific training, and therefore spent the period 1912-14 at Paris. There he made the acquaintance of the Abbé Breuil, the future professor of pre-history in the College de France, and Marcellin Boule, pro-fessor of palaeontology in the Museum.

Twenty-five years later, Teilhard still remembered this first meeting: 'Do you remember our first meeting, about mid-July 1912? . . . At two o'clock on that day, I first timidly rang at that door of the laboratory in the rue Valhubert that was later to become so familiar to me. You were exactly on the (sacred) eve of your departure for your holidays and very busy. . . . But you received me all the same. And . . . you made me the pro-position that I was to come to work with you at the school at Gaudry—your own school. And that is how, in five minutes almost, I began a new existence which has lasted until now—a life of research and adventure in the field of human palaeonto-logy. Never again, I believe, has Providence played such a leading role in my life."*

Shortly before, either the preceding year but perhaps as early as 1909, when the young palaeontologist was still study-ing theology, he had a stranger encounter. He met the "solicitor" Dawson, an archaeological amateur and discoverer of the notorious "Eoanthropus Dawsonii" which recent techniques revealed to be a fake in 1949. Dawson knew of the fossil speci-mens found by Teilhard in Sussex, and had invited him on three or four occasions to come and work at Piltdown where Teilhard made several minor finds. However Teilhard was not present at the discovery of the famous simian jawbone which was attributed to the non-existent "Eoanthropus". Neverthe-less, even after having been involved at a distance in this simulated encounter with Prehistoric Man, Teilhard was left with the memory of his youthful enthusiasm. In 1953, after the fraud had been discovered he confessed that it was "one of my most luminous palaeontological memories".

Fortunately, Pierre Teilhard de Chardin received more serious instruction and inspiration from his masters at Paris—Boule at the Institut de Paléontologie humaine, Jean Boussac at the Catholic Institute, Haug at the Sorbonne, and Cayeux at

* *L'Anthropologie*, 1937, pp. 599-600.

the Collège de France. At the same time the Abbé Breuil, soon
to be his friend, obliged him to seek the answers to certain
problems connected with prehistoric man which went beyond
the province of palaeontology.

1914. In normal circumstances, this would have been the
year of the Third Year for the young Jesuit, the year in which
he would take the solemn vows of his Order.

So far his career had been progressing in a straight line, but
it was to be broken by the impact of world events: although he
began his Third Year at Canterbury, in December 1914 he
was called up and sent to Vichy and then Clermont-Ferrand,
as a medical orderly. On January 20, 1915, he became stretcher-
bearer in a regiment of Moroccan sharpshooters, and later
joined the 4th mixed regiment of zouaves and sharpshooters
that was regarded as a crack regiment by the general Guyot de
Salins, and which was to be the first to be decorated with the
coveted red shoulder-lanyard.

The regiment and its inseparable stretcher-bearer Teilhard
saw service at Ypres and Champagne in 1915, Verdun in 1916,
Chemin-des-Dames in 1917, and the second Battle of the Marne
in 1918.

The distinguished intellectual proved himself a man under
fire: he would calmly crawl through the dark of no-man's land
to recover a dead comrade, and he had the gift of sympathy
which won him the friendship and respect of his superiors, and
the title of "sidi marabout" from the Moslem soldiers serving
in the regiment.

One would have thought that such conditions would hardly
have been suitable for research and reflection (Teilhard was in
the war of the trenches) but, none the less, Pierre Teilhard
found the time to observe and to write. It was while he was in
the trenches near Reims that he began to sketch out his geological thesis, and he filled several notebooks with his reflections.

His reflections were not to bring any radical change in his
intellectual orientation (for he was already heading in the
direction of specialisation in geology and palaeontology) but
they were to give his researches their true purpose. As a man
who had shared the inhuman or superhuman life of his fellows
and who had been so close to death, he could no longer study
the fossil man of the past without thinking of the man of today

and tomorrow. Rather than a collector of bones he would be a man in love with humanity, and a worshipper of matter, the matrix of man. We only have to read the titles of his surviving wartime writings to realise how his great religious themes were maturing hand in hand with his scientific knowledge: *Cosmic Life*; *Mastery of the World and the Reign of God*; *Christ in Matter*; *The Struggle against the Multitude*; *The Mystic Milieu*; *The Creative Union*; *Nostalgia of the Front*; *The Soul of the World*; *The Great Monad*; *My Universe*; *The Priest*; *Faith at Work*; *Forma Christi*.*

## PARIS, 1919-23

Pierre Teilhard de Chardin was demobilised on March 10, 1919, and soon completed the last academic formalities that were necessary before he could make his official entry into the scientific world.

He studied for his degree in natural science at the Sorbonne, following the lectures of Herouard and Robert. He obtained his geological certificate with the special mention of *good* in July 1919, and the certificates of botany and zoology without mentions in October 1919 and on March 19, 1920 respectively.

At Easter 1920 he took up seriously the thesis he had sketched out in the trenches at Reims on "The mammals of the French lower Eocene" and defended it on March 22, 1922.

It was in about 1920 that Teilhard began to make himself known to the scientific world not only by his publications (notably his monographs on the carnivorous fauna and primates of Quercy written before his thesis) but, above all, by his scientific links with scientists all over the world which often ripened into deep friendships and resulted in the creation of what Claude Cuénot was to call "the Teilhard network", including Paul Rivet, the future founder of the Musée de l'Homme in Paris, Stehlin of Basle, L. Dollo, the Belgian palaeontologist, Granger of the American Museum, and especially the Abbé Gaudefroy who had held the chair of geology at the Institut Catholique at Paris since 1919, and whom Teilhard had met through Breuil.

Through Gaudefroy, Teilhard made the acquaintance of M. Portal and his students of the École Normale, who, for

* Translation of French titles listed in the bibliography of Teilhard's works established by Cuénot (nos. 14-26, Cuénot).

many years, often invited him to come and lecture to them. It was Gaudefroy again who introduced him to Edouard Le Roy, thus beginning a loyal and friendly collaboration with the great Bergsonian philosopher. Finally, and most important, as Gaudefroy was a specialist in mineralogy he successfully requested that the chair of geology should be split into two posts; keeping the teaching of mineralogy for himself, and ceding the post of teacher of geology to Teilhard.

It was thus that Teilhard became teacher of geology at the Institut Catholique at Paris from 1920 to 1923.

## TIEN-TSIN, 1923-7

Father Teilhard was not to remain at the Institut Catholique. In 1923 he was entrusted with the mission of carrying out excavations in Central China, still retaining his chair, and being subsidised by the Museum. This was what he himself was later to call "the decisive event in my destiny".*

How had this come about?

In 1914, Father Licent, a Jesuit from the Province of Lille, had come to China where he later founded the Hoang-ho museum to contain his natural history collections. In order to identify fossilised relics of mammals, he had sent specimens to Marcellin Boule who had entrusted them to Teilhard, who then corresponded with Licent in order to obtain additional information. On July 4, 1921, and again on August 13, 1922, Father Licent had invited his Parisian colleague to come to China. In February 1923 Teilhard cabled that he was coming for one year and on May 23 he arrived at Tien-Tsin. It was not long before the two men realised the differences between them; one was a naturalist and, above all, an entomologist with no geological training whatever, and the other was a geological expert, a specialist in mammal palaeontology, man a of speculative and prophetic mind. Such differences were soon to give rise to disagreements.

In June 1923 the expedition that had been subsidised by the Museum got under way, with the plateau of the Ordos in central Mongolia as its destination. The two Jesuit scientists found irrefutable traces of palaeolithic Man in two sites, at Choei Tung K'eou, and on the banks of the river Sjaro-Osso-Gol.

* *Études*, July-August 1950, p. 127.

Teilhard eagerly informed Breuil and Boule of this real find. "For the first time", wrote Father Leroy, "the existence of palaeolithic man has been confirmed south of Ienissei. This discovery was a prelude to that of the Sinanthropus six years later, which was to be a sensational event in the study of Chinese pre-history."*

Once his mission had been accomplished Teilhard was to go straight back to his post at the Institut Catholique. There was another possibility; that the mission of summer 1923 would be followed by another mission in the spring of 1924. Teilhard asked his Rector, Mgr. Baudrillart, for orders. In the letters he wrote at this time it is clear that his real roots lay in Paris where he had left work in progress at the Museum, and that he was ready to come home.

But the Museum and the Institut Catholique, or rather Marcellin Boule and Mgr. Baudrillart, decided otherwise and Teilhard remained in China for a spring mission.

The winter of 1923-4 was spent in various activities; at Tien-Tsin where the material gathered during the "digs" at Ordos was classified, and Vialleton's† book attacking the classic theory of "transformism" was read and refuted, and at Peking where Teilhard often went to take part in a "little geological congress". How did the Jesuit geologist take to China? His impressions of the "little congress" at Peking throw some light on his attitude; for on January 14, 1924, he wrote: "What a difference there is between the kind of geology to be done here, and the collecting of shells in the Paris basin! This is the golden age of geological research in China."

In January and February 1924 two geological trips to the coal-fields of Kai-Ping and the mountains bordering the plain of Tcheli formed a prelude to the spring campaign of April-June. It was disappointing from the point of view of prehistoric archaeology, a little better from that of palaeontology, and most profitable of all in geology: "I am bringing back elements from a geological section of more than a thousand kilometres in a complicated country."‡

* Quoted by Cuénot, p. 70.
† *Membres et ceintures des Vertèbres tétrapodes, critique morphologique du Transformisme*, dated 1924.
‡ Cuénot, p. 80.

On September 13, Father Teilhard left China, after having prayed at the tomb of his elder sister Françoise who had died of black small-pox while she was mother superior of the Little Sisters of the Poor at Shanghai.

He returned to Paris in October 1924, and travelled in Europe, without losing contact with Paris, until 1926. He made a journey to England in 1925, with an interval of revising and bringing his notes up to date with the Abbé Breuil, and a period of spiritual retreat at Saint-Étienne in July 1925, besides various personal works, especially that on the "orthogenesis of Siphneidea", "one of his best claims to fame among the specialists" as Claude Cuénot wrote.

In the winter of 1925-6 his collaboration with Edouard Le Roy was closer than ever. Doubtless it is from the conversations, discussions, and exchanges of views of this period that the truly intellectual symbiosis between the two thinkers dates, and which was to be unequivocally proclaimed by Edouard Le Roy. In his *Exigence idéaliste et le fait de L'Évolution* (Idealist Necessity and the Fact of Evolution),* Le Roy showed that the main objections to "transformism" came from Vialleton, and he condensed the answers of the specialists by summarising several articles of Father Teilhard de Chardin's remarking "I have verbally discussed the views mentioned above for so long and on so many occasions with Father Teilhard, that even we ourselves are now unable to distinguish our respective contributions, and I must, therefore, content myself (as is practically inevitable) with making joint quotations, once and for all."

The Jesuit-geologist gave lectures in which science, philosophy, and religion all came together: he lectured to the Cercle du Luxembourg, to the pupils of the École Normale and Saint-Cloud, the Polytechnicians, and the groups of the U.S.I.C. At the Luxembourg, he lectured several times on evolution and he was to edit his views on the subject during the voyage from Marseilles to Shanghai under the title *Les fondements et le fond de l'idée de l'evolution* (Foundations and Basis of the Idea of Evolution).† To the pupils of the École Normale he explained how a

---

* Course of lectures given at the Collège de France, 1925-6, sixth lecture, p. 82.

† No. 84 in the Cuénot bibliography. Dated: Gulf of Bengal, Ascension Day, 1926.

Christian can be nourished by the *nourritures terrestres* without taking up the pagan position that Gide implied in his title. On another occasion, he used his *Milieu Divin* to preach to them during a three days' retreat. . . .

But in 1926 relations grew tense between Father Teilhard and his religious superiors in the Company of Jesus. A crisis arose which was to last throughout his life, in fair weather and foul. As a scientist he had not given rise to any anxiety for he was competent, and he patiently developed his theses in accordance with the data and in liaison with scientists all over the world. His religious attitude was exemplary and gave rise to not the slightest doubts. What disturbed the authorities of his Order were the theological implications of his reflections on scientific facts. As Claude Cuénot wrote, "What sparked off the crisis was a certain 'paper' the Father had written on the difficult problem of original sin." The author did not attempt to answer any questions, and did not put himself forward as a theologian, but merely offered certain provisional hypotheses suggested to him by his long reflections on what palaeontology tells us about the origins of man. It is quite unjustifiable to imagine that Teilhard had any intentions whatever of modifying dogma even in the smallest degree. But professional theologians and the Jesuit authorities who were in touch with the supreme authority of the Church were obliged to recognise the fact that his ideas, taken objectively, did not reflect the essentials of the dogma.

As a result, the decision was taken at the end of 1926 that Father Teilhard de Chardin would no longer be a teacher at the Institut Catholique, despite the protests of the Rector and the opposing opinion of the Council of the Faculty. We have no right to suppose that the Roman Catholic authorities had any intention of "punishing" Father Teilhard. All we can say is that they forbade him to devote himself to any public intellectual activity other than that of pure scientific research.

When notice of the official decision came to Teilhard in China where he had returned on June 10, he had time to prepare himself, and to accept the judgment—notably with the help of Edouard Le Roy who was later (in 1931) to give him the example of a total submission to the Church.

"I realise again, more clearly and more concretely, that

nothing spiritual or divine could happen to a Christian, or a cleric, except through the intermediary of the Church or its Order" (August 22).

"I now believe in the Church as 'Mediator' between God and the World, and I love it more explicitly and more truly than I did before the 'crisis'. And it seems to give me great peace" (August 22).

The separation from the Institut Catholique was to result in another much more formidable and completely unforeseen separation for Father Teilhard. By a kind of swing of the pendulum he was to become more Chinese than Parisian: he gradually accepted the fact that his "roots" were all that remained in Paris, as he had said on November 12, 1926, and January 16, 1927, and he finally confessed (February 27, 1927) that he found it easier to breathe in the Far East: "I still love Paris, you see. But it seems to me that I breathe even more freely among the international, lively, societies of the Pacific. . . . They are so free, so wide and so cordial!"

Let us not exaggerate. Teilhard was far from breaking all his sentimental and intellectual ties with Paris. Nevertheless, he gave up his salary (at least for the time) from the Museum, and from Boule—who was perhaps rather too "interested" in his museum—and he strengthened his relations with the Institut de France and especially with Alfred Lacroix, the permanent secretary at the Académie des Sciences. At the same time he felt himself strongly attracted towards the "National Geological Survey in China" whose headquarters was at Peking, which tended to take him away from Father Licent who remained based at Tien-Tsin. On February 27, 1927, Teilhard wrote that "The Geological Service at Peking is multiplying its offers".

When Teilhard returned to Paris on October 1, 1927, he was no longer a professor at the Institut Catholique, nor a recipient of a subsidy from the Museum, but, with the moral support of the Institut de France he had become the effective representative of French science in the Pacific area.

It was because he gradually let himself be drawn into the "Survey" that Father Teilhard was eventually to take part in the memorable discoveries at Chou-Kou-Tien.

At first he had not believed in the significance of Chou-Kou-Tien.

Doctor J. G. Andersson had discovered the fossil-bearing fissure towards 1921. The Austrian palaeontologist O. Zdansky found two humanoid teeth in 1922. Working under Black's direction, Doctor Bohlin had found a third tooth "of an undeniably human type" in 1927.

Teilhard had not yet been able to see for himself, and refrained from giving an opinion: he knew how to doubt. On November 12, 1926, he had written: "I am still not convinced of the human nature of the teeth in question" and on March 10, 1927: "I must confess that the photographs do not seem very convincing to me."

Nor did he look for some lucky windfall, or the chance of making some sensational find that would have made him into a "star". As arranged, he quietly returned to Paris in October 1927 and remained there until November 1928, seeing Le Roy again, meeting Valéry, making the acquaintance of Mgr. Bruno de Solages, working in the Museum, giving a series of ten lectures to the Tala group of pupils of the École Normale, and preaching to them at a retreat in February 1928.

In accordance with what he himself had called "this general principle in my life of never losing an opportunity for experimenting and research" (February 25, 1929), he did not go straight back to China. Invited by Henry de Monfreid and again sent on a mission by the Museum, Father Teilhard spent roughly two months in Abyssinia (late November 1928-beginning February, 1929) where he studied the geology of the Harrar and the Yemen. His observations were important enough for him to write: "All in all, I have enough material to be able to write two good memoirs at least, on Ethiopa and Somalia" (January 19, 1929).

At the beginning of February 1929 he embarked at Djibuti for Tien-Tsin where he arrived in March. In April, his "delightful friends" of the "Geological Survey of China" pressed him to join them as "Scientific adviser". On October 7 he was able to announce that henceforward he had an office in the headquarters of the "Survey".

From that date, it was inevitable that Father Teilhard was to play a leading role in the excavations at Chou-Kou-Tien:

"I am assuming an increasing responsibility for the geology and palaeontology (non-human) of the celebrated Chou-Kou-Tien" (December 6, 1929).

On December 28, 1929, he was able to write: "The greater part of a 'cerebral' skull of an undeformed *Sinanthropus* has been found at Chou-Kou-Tien (. . .) The jawbones are missing. As it is, the find is a striking one. In size noticeably or slightly larger than the *Pithecanthropus*, but with different frontal bosses and parietal bones (rather like those of the brain pan of Neanderthal man). Sub-orbital eye-sockets and post-orbital constriction more strongly marked than in Neanderthal Man." Later, on July 31, 1930: "On returning to Peking I had the surprise of beholding a second *Sinanthropus* skull, found during my absence" (six were to be found in all). And Father Teilhard went on to add: "I have great luck in being involved in this affair. Such opportunities as this end by making me uniquely and madly in love with the Divine Influence which governs the World." Decidedly, such a love was enough to recompense for someone who had irrevocably devoted his life to scientific research and the possession of God. Nothing less would have sufficed for Teilhard to have serenely continued with his scientific work and to have maintained his friendly relations with everyone, at a time of great internal stress: what was his future to be? Should he, or should he not leave the Company of Jesus?

But the same letter goes on to say: "It seems to me that I have never been more passionate and solid in my faith in the Universe, and, at the same time, more profoundly indifferent to what is ordinarily human in the world." When writing these lines more than a year had gone by since what he had carelessly called "the little crisis"; it had left only two marks on him: his passion for "the Universal Affair in which we are engaged by our existence" and the loss of all "Ability to take pleasure in (or to desire) anything whatever concerning myself", in a word, "a kind of passionate indifference" (December 6, 1929).

He was, therefore, fighting on two fronts: on one hand, he was fighting against himself and for the conquest of inner peace, and on the other, he was fighting a World that was jealous of its secrets, in order to conquer it through knowledge.

The part played by Teilhard in the discovery of the *Sinan-*

*thropus* can be defined as follows, after the detailed analyses made by Cuénot:

Before Chou-Kou-Tien, Teilhard and Licent had already furnished the proof of the existence of prehistoric man in China.

Andersson, Zdansky, Black and Bohlin had unearthed teeth, jaw-bones and skulls.

Teilhard had demonstrated the great age of the remains of the *Sinanthropus* and had dated them in the old Quaternary period.

If not the first, Teilhard had at least been one of the first with, or after, Breuil, to recognise that the *Sinanthropus* was a *faber* (maker and user of tools), on the basis of chipped stones, traces of fire and human habitation.

But as a palaeontologist Father Teilhard had not forgotten that the first key to the interpretation of the evidence unearthed was that supplied by geology.

As a geologist he was gradually to annex the whole of China as his province. In May-June 1929, he explored the northern Asian region almost as far as Siberia in the company of Father Licent: "At one swoop I have almost doubled my domain" (June 16, 1929). In June-July, 1929, he discovered the Shansi and the Shensi with the Chinese geologist Young. In February 1930 he was again in the Shansi, in the south of the region, with Barbour. In June-July 1930 he took part in an American Central Asian expedition (Kalgan, the Gobi Desert). It was with reason that he could write on two occasions (September and October 1929) that "without any great merit on his part" he found himself to be "one of the Europeans (and even one of the Chinese) who had seen the most of Northern China, just as our geological knowledge of this great country is beginning to be organised".

If the plan that Father Teilhard had submitted for the approval of his superiors in 1927 is borne in mind—"That I may be allowed the time in Paris to publish my findings and to make contact again with the scientific world (eighteen months) before returning to China for another eighteen months (finding the money for the voyage myself)" and "oscillating between Paris and Tien-Tsin, with headquarters in the latter place if thought necessary—that is to say continuing what I have been doing since 1923"—then it would seem evident that he had decided that the time had come to return to Paris.

In fact, he returned by the Trans-Siberian express in September 1930, for a short three-months' stay during which he agreed to give a lecture to the students of the École Normale, and another four lectures to the Marcel Légaut group. It is easy to guess the reason why Teilhard wanted to "oscillate" between Paris and the excavation site: in the field, and in the company of scientists who forebore to ask themselves what the result of their efforts might be, he was able to reconstruct the past of the world and the first men. In Paris, he was able to confide his secret ideas, his inner vision of the Creation, the Incarnation, and the Eschatology as suggested to him by his specialist's convictions, to an avid and prepared audience.

But was it possible for him to forget that this vision, as he had formed it, had not satisfied the professional theologians?

Even if he was tempted to forget it, someone was going to take it upon himself to remind him of it. Father Teilhard had to make a trip to the United States where he was to give lectures and hold a number of preliminary meetings with the geologists of Mongolia before setting off on the "Croisière Jaune" expedition. In the course of preparation for this expedition he was also to meet the French ambassador, Paul Claudel . . .

Now, Claudel was a cosmic poet as Jacques Madaule has called him, but he was also first and foremost a Thomist poet, as he himself had said, and he could not bear the idea of a literature that had a scientific basis and which was partly conjectural. Claudel went straight to God, in his conceptions of Man as a being who is marked by the stigmata of his destiny and his final destination. "The Universe is simply a total means of not being That which is!"*

Teilhard felt himself entirely misunderstood by Claudel.

By way of contrast, Teilhard met with complete success in his dealings with the National Geographic Society at Washington: they gave the same subsidy for the Citroën Mission's famous "Croisière Jaune" as they had given to Byrd for his voyage to the South Pole.

In March 1932 Teilhard was back in China once more.

* _Art poetique_, p. 145.

THE "CROISIÈRE JAUNE", JUNE 1931-FEBRUARY 1932

The Citroën firm had been sounding Father Teilhard since 1929: "The Citroën trans-Asiatic mission has been pressing me with great insistence (on behalf of the Museum and the Ministries) to accompany them on their way through China. If this *trip* [*in English in the original text*] can be combined with some useful work which would be agreeable to the 'Survey' then I may agree" (September 29, 1929).

At first, he was not very enthusiastic: "At the most all the project will amount to will be making the sort of journey I have been undertaking since 1923, in a caterpillar-truck (October 7, 1929).

In February 1930 his attitude had changed: "I will have the whole spring of 1931 in which to visit western China by car, in the caravan leaving Peking to meet the Mission. I shall then be taken from Peking as far as Hanoi by the *Croisière*, acting as their geologist and as the representative of the Chinese Geological Service. Under these conditions, I have accepted the offer (Lyons has given me complete liberty)." By Lyons he meant his Jesuit superiors in the province of Lyons.

As it turned out, this splendid programme was somewhat spoilt by the Soviets who made it difficult for the two motorised columns to join up, and by the bandits who infested the region.

It is not our purpose to relate the whole story of the *Croisière*:* a few main points and dates will suffice:

Father Teilhard joined the "China Group" at Kalgan (north-west of Peking) on May 12, 1931. The group travelled towards Turkestan along the edge of the Gobi Desert, its mission being to join up with the other group in the heart of Central Asia. It halted at Soutcheou on June 11-21; at the Hami oasis on June 28-July 1; at Turfan on July 5-17; the planned junction was made on October 2 at Aksou near the Russian frontier. This meeting was followed by the return, this time by a slightly different route. On January 1, 1932, Father Teilhard said Mass at the Lian-Tcheou Mission, in the presence of all the members of the *Croisière Jaune*, not one of whom was a practising Catholic. On January 28, the column was attacked

---

* See Georges Lefèvre, *La Croisière Jaune*, Plon, 1952. Louis Audouin Dubreuil, *Sur la route de la soie*, Plon, 1935, and André Reymond, *Résultats scientifiques d'un voyage en Asie centrale*, Revue de Géographie physique, 1938.

by Chinese bandits. On January 30, the *Croisière* had reached the railway terminus at Pao-Teo.

"We ended up by arriving in Peking (February 12) . . . after a journey's end which was marked by magnificent weather, moderate cold (not more than 30°C. at night), and the usual incidents of a voyage in China (12 bullets in one of our trucks without any casualties)" (February 21, 1932).

What were the results of the *Croisière Jaune?*

Complete triumph or total failure? Each of these extreme judgements has been upheld.

In reality, since the main point of the *Croisière* was to test the mechanical performance of the trucks, the scientific objectives of the *Croisière* had been somewhat neglected. Moreover, the insecure conditions and the unhealthiness of the region traversed had exposed the members to disproportionately high risks in view of the results finally obtained.

Still, the expedition's geologist did not appear to be dissatisfied:

"Despite unfavourable working conditions (rapid rate of travel without adjustable halts at interesting points), I have managed to achieve my purpose of linking up the geology of China and that of Central Asia. Formations and structures continue in an unexpected manner. Not to have made this survey would have been a great loss to me in the future. Few fossils, unfortunately, and nothing of any great age from the prehistoric point of view" (July 7, 1931).

From the personal point of view, Father Teilhard's sojourn among unbelievers and non-practising Catholics had been a sort of compulsory stay in a world which was the exact opposite of his own inner world. He had suffered from being unable to withdraw into solitude in order to meditate, and from having been the target for witticisms that were never unkind but always painful because they were made by those who never realised the mystery of his inner life. But he clearly profited from this contact with every sort of secular mentality, for he ended by knowing how to talk to his companions and how not to talk to them, and he was able to divine how Christianity should be presented to them so that they might have a chance of hearing the message of Christ and the Church without any misunderstanding. He let his innermost self, the very centre of

his spiritual existence as a priest and as a Jesuit always faithful
to his calling and his Order, admit a secular spirit which he
was always to include in his spiritual make-up and which was
to allow him both to understand the spirit of laymen and to be
understood by them.

Georges-Marie Haardt, the leader of the *Croisière Jaune*, had
died at Hong Kong from an infectious disease. Father Teilhard
remained in touch with his widow, who had to be consoled
and given courage. This is how he spoke to her:

"He is no longer here. And he is no longer waiting for you
here. To speak as a Christian (for this is what we are, in the
final resort, even if it is in a somewhat renovated manner),
Georges-Marie has now found the God he was looking for
throughout his heroic journeyings" (February 3, 1936).

To be Christian, in a "somewhat renovated manner": this
is what Teilhard was proposing to those who were Christians
only in name.

### PEKING, 1932-46

Speaking of the *Croisière Jaune*, Father Teilhard had written:
"This is the last time I shall journey in this way. I envisage new
horizons, but probably different ones, more suitable to my age
and the sort of work I can now undertake."

There was no faltering of the seeker's determination: on the
contrary, for he was now about to take the measure of the World
and to encompass it with a mind fortified by his frequent
travels and the elaborate network of his collaborators. But in
order to undertake the study of the Asian continent in its
entirety, new mechanical, financial and institutional resources
were called for. The "tranquil pace of the mules of Shansi"
had given way to the "majestic rhythm of the Citroën cater-
pillar trucks", and geology was soon to have need of the
"speed of the American Dodges".*

Father Teilhard was to devote himself entirely to obtaining
new means of making a wider survey than any before.

This was to be his positive, generous answer when he was
forbidden to publish anything extra-scientific: "Have seen
Father —— here, who brought me the two definitive criticisms

* *La carrière scientifique du P. Teilhard de Chardin, Études,* July-August 1950,
p. 127.

of the *Milieu Divin*. Both are very favourable, except (in one of them) for a request for precision with regard to the 'Sense of the Cross', which I think I should easily be able to satisfy. A pity that everything has been stopped" (Christmas 1932).

Everything was stopped. Father Teilhard gave up publishing anything of a purely religious nature and agreed to what he was to call (February 26, 1933) "The defeat of my literature". In 1935, when a friend seemed prepared to publish *Les Fondements et le Fond de l'idée d'Évolution*, *L'Esprit de la Terre*, and *Comment Je crois*, Teilhard confided to him: "I do not dare to hope for so much!" (July 29, 1935).

Moreover, on May 25, 1938, he declared "Rome has informed me that I should refuse any post or title that may be offered to me in Paris." The following year he was to declare that he had not even been tempted by a certain offer of a post as teacher in the Museum (February 11, 1936).

Since speculation, or, at least, communication of his thoughts to the public in book form, was forbidden to him, Father Teilhard believed at a certain moment (February 26, 1933), that his vocation was to become that of *action*: to free others by words and by confidential writings from "the chains that it took him twenty years to break away from himself". These "chains" were, no doubt, the same as the "cloak" that the new Elias let fall from his shoulders (in: *La Puissance spirituelle de la Matière*): "the weight of all that is false, narrow, tyrannical, *artificial*, and *human* in Humanity".

But, in reality, Father Teilhard's need to speculate was stronger than any other passion . . . or resolution. "At present, it hardly matters to me whether I am printed or not. What I see is infinitely greater than all inertia and all obstacles" (September 1934). In June 1935 he confessed: "Apart from a small number of contributions of a scientific nature, my best personal achievement, so far, has been to obtain a clearer inner picture of new possible developments in my 'philosophy'."

A man like Teilhard is always true to himself, even in submission.

For it is because his submission was not merely a matter of words, but something which came from his heart, his spirit and his entire body that Teilhard was to become literally a man of the earth.

"The paradox", wrote Claude Cuénot (p. 332), "of the life of a scientist whose brilliant successes from 1926 onwards were due to a series of exiles accepted in a way that shows the full measure of Father Teilhard's fidelity to his Order."

One might go further and ask what Teilhard's work would have amounted to as a geologist and palaeontologist had he made a "career" in Paris. Certainly he would, of his own volition, have gone out from Paris into the field from time to time. But would he have soaked himself in data to the same extent, would he have kept such a tight hold on his information network, made the same discoveries, and inspired research in such a vast field in the same way? Would he have been able to keep present in his mind all that multitude of details and impressions which alone allow that sudden flash of intuition which is known as the mark of a "genius"?

The proof is simple: during his second period in Paris the decrease in his scientific output was due to his lack of contact with the field, and it was his renewal of contact with the field in South Africa in 1951 which was immediately to inspire him. There is justification for thinking that if he had remained a teacher of geology, and a hundred per cent Parisian, he would have run the risk of being drawn by his temperament towards pure religious speculation without any experimental basis.

Moreover, when he had been nominated teacher at the Institut Catholique in Paris, he had spontaneously written: "Instead of this teacher's post, I would naturally have preferred a post as prospector at Beirut, Shanghai, or Trichinopoly, where they need people."*

Everything was as if obedience to his superiors was to be the chance for him to follow his primary scientific vocation and to take geological prospecting of the earth to a hitherto unattained degree of depth and universality.

Firstly, Father Teilhard cultivated his friendly and scientific contacts throughout the scientific world, and made new ones, from Paris where he kept his "roots" to Asia where he was assured of collaborators of every nationality: Chinese such as Peï and Wong, Swedish such as Hedin and Norin, the Americans, Granger, Osborn, Simpson, Gregory, Barbour, Helmut

---

* Father Pierre Leroy, *Le P. Teilhard de Chardin, tel que je l'ai connu*, p. 24. *Études*, July-August 1950, p. 128.

de Terra, and the Germans, Wendereich and von Koenigswald. Long ago Teilhard had confessed: "I dote on these internationalists" (November 1926), and he went on to say "At the same time that I was weaving, I hope, some threads for my web (the web of possible influences), I felt myself confirmed as an incorrigible internationalist, or, more precisely, a terrestrian" (December 1926). It was in 1926 that he had encouraged Hedin to "go over to the Chinese" despite the objections and reservations of his best European friends.

"Web of influences" according to Teilhard.

"Teilhard's network", wrote Claude Cuénot, who added, "a veritable network, with the Father holding the threads firmly, and acting as its liaison agent, or rather as its chief of staff, capable, like a water-diviner, of making a stream of American money gush forth, or at least of canalising it for the greater benefit of palaeontology."

His vocation for action did not only imply "liberation" in the religious sense for it was first directed towards "animating" in the scientific field. By "animating" Teilhard meant: directing, making demands, modifying. . . . He became director of studies for his Chinese colleague Peï who was preparing his thesis at the Sorbonne under the aegis of the Abbé Breuil, exerting an inspiring, modifying, and stimulating influence. Teilhard even told von Koenigswald who was already famous, though still young, that proof should be more substantial and that conclusions should only be made with caution, Teilhard also exerted a moderating influence on his former master and constant friend, the Abbé Breuil: as, for instance, when the Abbé seemed too quickly disposed to believe in the perfection of the stone and bone carving prowess of the *Sinanthropus*. Teilhard also controlled and supervised the Chinese who continued to prospect at Chou-Kou-Tien, thus giving them a progressive training.

The network which served him also obliged him to make new researches and discoveries, for the very existence of this network made it necessary to collect and synthetise the various scattered data that it allowed him to obtain; he had also to throw light on this data by continually widening the field of his observations. With this aim in view Teilhard was to make new trips to the Far East, while continuing to direct the excavations at Chou-Kou-Tien.

For the moment, then, the excavations went on at Chou-Kou-Tien although Teilhard only spent brief periods in China between 1934 and 1938, the work being in the hands of Chinese scientists who owed a great part of their training to Teilhard— especially Peï and Wong. As a matter of fact, the site had yielded up its main secret with the *Sinanthropus* but this would only become a certainty once the site had been thoroughly sifted. It was then found that the site had been successively inhabited by *Cynocephali*, the *Sinanthropus*, and lastly, *Homo Sapiens*, traces of bone work proving the presence of this last. Thus, in 1933, 1936, and 1937, one discovery followed another, despite the Japanese invasion which as early as 1933 had obliged the "Survey" to move its books and collections. The last "dig" directed by Teilhard came to an end on July 6, 1937, when Chou-Kou-Tien suddenly became part of the "no man's land" between the Japanese and the Red forces.

Nevertheless, the study of the site at Chou-Kou-Tien could not be an end in itself, for the good reason that it did not contain its own explanation from the geological point of view. In 1932 Teilhard was already writing that the correct procedure was to "follow the deposits of the fissures and to scratch around Peking and Malaya, from North to South" (June 5, 1932). In order to understand the geological significance of Chou-Kou-Tien it was necessary to put the site into the context of China and the whole of Asia. "In order to place the new and sensational fossil man and to give him his correct interpretation, nothing less was needed than a stratigraphic, physiographic and palaeontological revision of the whole of the Quaternary of the Far East. (...) to this central problem, whose ramifications would take him in succession (thanks to the powerful assistance of various American foundations and universities) to India, Burma and Java, (...) Father Teilhard has devoted all the fullness and authority of his experience during the last fifteen years of his stay in the Far East."*

It was thus, in accordance with the necessities of scientific explanation, that Father Teilhard covered the area around Chou-Kou-Tien, after having explored the Shansi in 1932 and 1933, and then determinedly made his way towards south

* *Études*, July-August 1950, p. 128.

China, even crossing the frontier to penetrate into Malaya, Burma and Java.

In this way, he allowed himself to be drawn by Barbour on to the route to Chinese Tibet: 'Since Easter (and following the plan drawn up with Black), I have been prospecting in the Yang-Tse from Nanking to the first ranges of Tibet. Very interesting geologically—but not very *promising* [in English in the original] from the prehistoric point of view" (June 25, 1934).

In July 1934 he made an expedition into the Shansi and the Honan in order to tie up the Tertiary and Quaternary formations of northern and southern China: "A magnificent journey which revealed a new third part of China to me. Still a third to be done (the southernmost) and then I think we shall begin to throw some light on the Chinese Tertiary and Quaternary" (July 13, 1934).

In January 1935, he left for the province of Canton. Observations made by Teilhard there showed that there was an equivalence between the *Sinanthropus* layers in northern China and the *Pithecanthropus* layers in Java. It was only then that Chou-Kou-Tien began to make sense in its entirety. But in order to gain a complete picture it was necessary to go beyond the bounds of China.

As a result Teilhard spent September-December 1935 in India for the first time, where he verified his geological hypotheses and helped Terra and Patterson to complete their own hypotheses on Indian prehistory.

At the beginning of 1936 he made a detour to Java, where von Koenigswald wanted to show him a second *Pithecanthropus* skull which had just been found at Sangiran and which was more complete than the first.

At the end of July 1936, the indefatigable Father spent another three weeks in the Shansi as he needed additional data on the region.

Early in 1938 he went to Burma with Helmut de Terra and Movius.

The synthesis grew steadily: "I believe that we now have the necessary elements for making a first approximate linkage between the pleio-pleistocene series of Southern China, Northern India, and perhaps Malaya, which, in my mind, was the principal aim of this little expedition" (March 16, 1938).

"This", said Father Leroy, "was his last expedition in the field."*

On March 24, 1938, Teilhard left again for Java where von Koenigswald was continually making new discoveries: Teilhard hoped that his friend would eventually benefit from the powerful aid of the Carnegie Foundation.

Teilhard gave proof of an admirable physical endurance and mental determination in all his travels throughout Asia and China, but events began to overtake him: the Japanese occupation made it practically impossible to go on working at Chou-Kou-Tien and he had to go back to the laboratory and use a typewriter instead of a hammer and pick-axe. It was not long before Father Licent himself was obliged to leave his museum at Tien-Tsin.

Teilhard felt the need for a solid base for his activities somewhere in the world. On October 1, 1937, he sent a report to the director of the third section of the Hautes Études with the aim of obtaining the establishment of a Laboratoire des Hautes Études for research in continental geology, considered in its relation to human palaeontology. The authorities at Rome accepted the project on April 26, 1938 and on May 27 the minister, Jean Zay, created the Laboratory. Unfortunately this Institution, which had been specially set up to meet Teilhard's requirements, was never to function as the war was soon to keep the director of the Parisian laboratory in China.

In the meantime, it was vital that Teilhard should return to France to organise his "Labo". On the way back he made several detours, one towards the end of 1938 to Japan to defend the interests of world science in China, and a second to see Granger in New York. He finally arrived in Paris in November, and lectured at Toulouse (on the invitation of Mgr. Bruno de Solages). In Paris he returned to his apostolic task of lecturing on doctrinal subjects to restricted circles. He also saw Lecomte du Noüy whom he had met on the *Île de France* while sailing from New York to Le Havre.

On June 23, 1939, he embarked once again for China, with the intention of making a rapid visit. Unfortunately events were to turn his visit into an interminable captivity. The world

* *Pierre Teilhard de Chardin tel que je l'ai connu*, p. 38.

War and the occupation of China by the Japanese prevented
nearly all his travelling plans from being realised: it was the
most he could do to go to Tien-Tsin in June 1940 to move the
museum which had been threatened by the floods of 1939.

He was, therefore, obliged to concentrate on laboratory
work and to examine and describe all the material that had
been accumulated in drawers and chests. This necessity to
classify and analyse was soon replaced in Teilhard's mind by a
grandiose project—might it not be possible to describe the
entire zoological evolution of China? In accordance with his
special talents it would simply amount to a complete description of the mammiferous fossils of China.*

Secondly, as the Hoang-ho Païi-Ho museum had to be completely evacuated to Peking, the problem of its transformation
arose. Could it be made into a research institute? As a matter
of fact it became the Institute of Geo-biology which published
a number of monographs, the first issue including Teilhard's
definition of what he meant by Geo-biology. He also spent
much of his time reading books of a general nature, literary
and philosophical works,† and writing his first major work *The
Phenomenon of Man*. He was hard at work on it in 1940 and
sent it to Rome the following year to be approved by the censor.
In 1944 Teilhard was told that his book had been rejected. He
had to revise and correct it. . . .

May 8, 1945. "V Day. Relief—but not joy—because in
itself—at least for the moment—this brutal victory of Man over
Man is not a victory for Humanity."

He had followed all the phases of the war with the feeling
that he was a distant witness to some absurd and cruel game,
but his confidence was still unshaken in the movement that
was to bring the World perpetually nearer to Unity through
Love, to the Centre where all things meet.

### PARIS, 1946-51

From many points of view the remaining years of Teilhard's
life should have been a time of rich harvests. He was now sixty-
five years old and field work had become increasingly painful

---

\* *Chinese fossil mammals . . . a complete bibliography analysed, tabulated,
annotated and indexed* (Cuénot bibliography, no. 223).

† Cuénot has tried to reconstruct the list, pp. 290-1.

for him. The war conditions in Peking and the post-war atmosphere in Paris neither allowed nor offered him any more chances to make fruitful contacts with the soil and the stones of the earth. Due to the war, the "Laboratory of Geology applied to Man" in Paris did not have any real activity and the Institute of Geo-biology at Peking had to take its place at a great distance. In 1947 Teilhard was appointed director of Research in the National Scientific Research Centre which subsidised him, but none of this was worth the most modest excavation.

When he left Peking even Teilhard's religious thought seemed to have reached its point of climax. Far from coming to a full stop or stagnating, it was to become increasingly well defined, but there were to be no more sudden great flashes of intuition.

Teilhard returned to France at the beginning of May 1946, leaving books and papers behind him in what was soon to become the Peoples' Republic of China. Nevertheless, he took back his most precious manuscripts, notably that of *The Phenomenon of Man* and on June 26, 1946, he wrote that he was awaiting the two new revised versions of his book which were being typed in triplicate.

Back in Paris, Teilhard was once again to win the friendship of the men he encountered. But, at the same time, he was to realise that there was an irreducible opposition between his own thought and the philosophical systems that had then become fashionable.

His friends included Roger Lévy, an expert on the Pacific, and those who gathered under Paul Rivet, already well known to Teilhard, at the Musée de l'Homme once a week. And from quite another quarter, Julian Huxley, who may perhaps have been the only Anglo-Saxon to have ever understood Teilhard, because he had reached the same conclusions by a different route.

Who were his adversaries?

In its various aspects, existentialism opposed Teilhard's thought with its pessimistic, defiant conception of matter and technique. Concerning the question: "To what extent does the material organisation of humanity take it towards a point of spiritual maturity?" Teilhard realised how greatly Gabriel

Marcel's thought was opposed to his own. Where Teilhard saw a spiritualisation of matter itself due to the collective effort to know it and to master it, Marcel saw a new kind of Prometheus at work in an anti-Christian direction. To the question "What is the world's purpose?" Teilhard's answer would be "The world is the matrix of the spirit" while Louis Lavelle would answer: the world only serves man if man liberates himself from it.

Teilhard opposed that purely interior and subjective phenomenology which is the indispensable introduction to existentialism, with his own kind of all-embracing "phenomenology", bearing on a world taken in all its materiality. "I do not understand how one can call oneself a 'phenomenologist' and write whole books without even mentioning or naming Cosmogenesis and Evolution" (April 11, 1953).

Basically, it seemed to Teilhard that all these philosophies were existing in a pre-Galilean universe. Only marxism, and, perhaps, evolutionist pantheism, seemed to contain assimilable elements, on condition, it is true, that they were freshly considered and completely digested.

In order to spread his ideas which were always popular with many young secular and lay followers, even if they were quite different from the fashionable philosophies of the time, Teilhard held a number of meetings, refusing to give lectures—which was forbidden to him: his meetings were sometimes in the form of a debate at the "Union Catholique des Scientifiques français", and were also held on several occasions at the "Centre Catholique des Intellectuels français", and at the homes of scientists or in salons frequented by scientists.

On the night of June 1/2 he was suddenly hit by a heart attack, perhaps brought on by his injections against yellow fever. He fell into a coma on the way to the clinic of Les Frères de Saint-Jean-de-Dieu, and his condition was very grave for the next fortnight. For the rest of his life his health was always threatened and precautions became necessary, with no more travel by air and no more long walks.

His physical trials were followed by a new spiritual crisis, for in September 1947 high authorities forbade him to write on philosophical or theological questions. There was no longer any question of publishing *The Phenomenon of Man*. In the years preceding the Papal encyclical *Humani generis*, there was too

much intellectual ferment for the Church to consider it oppor-
tune to publish a work which could only be read with profit by
readers whose philosophical and theological understanding
was as great as their scientific understanding. Such tendencies
became the object of public controversies as shown by two
antithetically opposed publications: *Pour la défense de la théologie*
and *Pour l'honneur de la théologie.** Teilhard's superiors were
unable to resolve the debate: theologians were to be good
theologians, and scientists were to be good scientists. . . . But
the frontiers between theology and science were not always as
well defined as those in high places wished them to be. When
Teilhard wrote: *Le rebondissement humain de l'évolution et ses
conséquences,*† was this still only a scientific paper, or was it [also]
theology as well? In the eyes of those whose function it was to
act as his judges Teilhard risked appearing, if not as an un-
submissive son of the Church, at least as an independent and
perhaps obstinate thinker.

Such was the situation in 1948 when the moment came for the
Abbé Breuil to retire from his post as professor at the Collège de
France. Could he not be replaced by Teilhard, whose scientific
work would thus be given immense recognition? Paul Rivet
proposed Teilhard who, as a good Jesuit, went to receive
orders in Rome, after a brief trip to America where the subject
of South Africa came up for the first time. . . .

Early in October 1948 he arrived in the Eternal City. He
felt at home there, and comforted by the trusting and warm
welcome given him by his superiors. But with regard to the
proposed post at the Collège de France, the answer was in the
negative. As for the problem of *The Phenomenon of Man*, which
had still to be resolved, there was no decision as yet. As a result,
from December 1948 Teilhard began work on a new and more
strictly scientific exposition of his thought: it was in fact to be
the outline of a course of *Anthropogenesis* ("Geo-biological
observations on the position, the structure and the possible
ultra-development of Humanity"), which was to serve him as
the basis for a series of lectures at the Sorbonne in February
1949. The final result was the book *Le Groupe zoologique humain,*

* Signed by Mgr. Bruno de Solages (*Bulletin de littérature ecclésiastique*,
Toulouse, no. 2, April-June 1947).

† *Revue des questions scientifiques*, April 20, 1948.

work which, Claude Cuénot tells us "the Father valued, in reality, far more than *The Phenomenon of Man*".*

His trips in quick succession to New York and Rome proved too much for his already weakened health. At Easter 1949 he was kept at Saint-Germain-en-Laye until June 6 by an attack of pleurisy. It was there that he finished revising *Le Groupe zoologique humain*. In February 1950 he was able to submit the manuscript to the Roman censor, not without hope, since he had wished this new work to be more purely scientific than *The Phenomenon of Man*. However, the answer on June 28 was still in the negative: the book still went beyond the bounds of science, strictly speaking.

Was Teilhard discouraged? He was to try to reconcile obedience to his superiors with adherence to a line which he believed came from God and led to God.

"How can I stop, without failing in my profoundest duties towards God and towards men? ... I have, therefore, decided to continue as before—relying on the fortunes or more exactly on the legitimacy of my cause. I know that all the heretics have said this. But generally their attitude was not intended to magnify Christ above all, which is precisely the only thing with which I can be reproached."

"To continue as before" . . . this meant: to continue to write letters and papers, to allow himself to be invited to salons and private meetings, to hold courses and series of lectures at the Sorbonne. He was to undertake no action that could be even remotely construed as disobedient, but in the sphere of what he was allowed to do, he was to do everything to diffuse his ideas. Accordingly, he presented himself as a candidate at the Institut de France where he was elected on May 22, 1950. "As you know, this election to the Institut only interests me in so far as it will armour me against certain attacks or, to use another metaphor, in so far as it will make my shafts more penetrating" (May 14, 1950).

. . . "All the heretics have said this": Teilhard realised this all the more as he was being sent essays and projects from various people whose orthodoxy did not always match his own. It was

---

* p. 347. Cf. Tresmontant, *Introduction à la pensée du P. Teilhard de Chardin*, p. 133: "Even in Teilhard's own opinion . . ., The Human Phenomenon had been surpassed, as he wrote us in these last recent years."

his turn to become a judge: "I do not see very well", he wrote to one correspondent, "how an essay of this nature can be given the *imprimatur*, not only because of the frankness of its criticisms,—but because of the possible ambiguities and confusions that might arise from the expressions" (October 21, 1949). There was no doubt in Teilhard's mind that a certain norm of faith was indispensable and that it should be possible to deduce a rule from it to permit one to judge the value of a formula. As a consequence his conclusions were as firm as they had been in 1948, and maybe even more precise:

"I have realised (at Saint Peter's (Rome), only there), how much Christianity is a phenomenon on its own (the 'Christian phenomena', I was right) with its paradoxical but irrefutable and efficacious assurance that it represents the earthly extremity of an 'arch' reaching from Man to what is above Man" (October 15, 1948).

"It is only in the tree of Rome, taken in its entirety, that I can see a biological support both sufficiently vast and differentiated to achieve and to strengthen the awaited transformation" (i.e. the transformation of humanity) (October 4, 1950).

This conviction was to become increasingly strong until the very end: "The more I come to the end of my life, the more I feel myself indissolubly attached to a Christian course, outside which I can see no complete valorisation (nor, above all, any possible *amorisation*) [integration by love: a term invented by Teilhard. Trans.] for what we call evolution" (January 25, 1955, three months before his death).

And even more briefly, his declaration to Father Bergounioux:

"If the Church falls, all is lost!"

Teilhard did not ignore the existence of other institutions aiming at the unification of humanity. As early as 1947, UNESCO, represented by Torrès-Bodet, had been asking for his advice. He gave it, notably with regard to the racial problem, but in a way that could not please a great many people: he wrote (July 27, 1950) that: "the different races are not equal but complement each other". Such an attitude could not receive the approval of UNESCO. It was therefore not on this international organisation but on his newly found friend Julian Huxley (who had been the director of UNESCO), that he could depend for the foundation of the dreamed of Institute for the study and control of the human forces of Self-(Ultra) evolution. A large correspondence exists between Teilhard and Huxley, dating from 1950, which shows that the religious-scientist and the atheist-biologist were equally concerned for the future of the human race. None the less, a year later Teilhard declared that he had "a more exact idea" of the road he had to take "following a different course and with quite a different crew from that of Huxley's" (July 11, 1951).

Full of projects, Teilhard was far from being broken in spirit. Since he was not allowed to publish it, he divulged his thought by every means allowed to him, to such an extent that the "High Command (of his Order) became rather nervous about him", as Claude Cuénot wrote, adding, "The Father isn't doing much to bring about a *détente*." He was doing some-thing else instead: he left for South Africa and explained in a letter to the General of the Order: "I have great hopes that my absence from Europe will allow all the commotion about me, that may have disturbed you recently, to die down" (October 1951). He may also have remembered that his superiors pre-ferred to see him at work in his own special sphere, in the field, rather than in Paris among the intellectuals.

His decision to visit South Africa seems to have had a calming influence on Teilhard, which lasted throughout the following years.

In answer to an "extremely kind and comprehensive letter from a superior", he wrote, "The first time a superior has asked me to think freely and constructively before him. . . . Such gestures do more to draw me closer to the Order than any amount of decrees" (August 21, 1952).

"I am on the friendliest of terms with my Order" (August 8, 1952).

In 1954, he obtained permission to go to Paris, doubtless for only a short time, and without great difficulty.

### THE UNITED STATES, 1951-5

Teilhard de Chardin was full of projects and they were all concerned with scientific research. As early as 1950 he had spoken of the possibility of visiting South Africa. "The similarity of the terrain where the Australopithecinae had been found

with that where the Sinanthropus had been buried had made
the South-African prospectors decide to call for the collaboration of a specialist."*

The following year he carried out his intention, it being
justified on one hand as his duty as a geologist and palaeontologist, and on the other hand, as a splendid gesture of pride,
obedience, and charity: "It seems clear to me that this plunge
back into geology is the gesture for me to make. But it is
precisely this gesture that is going to demand a certain effort.
As God wills!" (May 9, 1951).

His letter to the General of the Jesuits,† gives us an idea of
the true significance of this gesture: "Evidently I cannot give
up my own inner search—for this would result in an inner
catastrophe and in my being disloyal to my most cherished
vocation—but (and this has been the case for some months), I
am no longer propagating my ideas, but am only trying to
gain a deeper personal insight into them" (Cape Town,
October 12, 1951). This, then, was the meaning of his great
voyage to South Africa, South America and the United States.

With the encouragement of Rome and the financial support
of the *Viking Fund* (soon to become the *Wenner Gren Foundation
for Anthropological Research*), Teilhard set off for South Africa,
stopping first at London in July 1951. There he was asked to
draw up a plan for the co-ordination of researches. On his
arrival in Johannesburg on August 1, the plan had been drawn
up and the work allotted.

The objects of the expedition were as follows:

1. "to continue the investigations of the Australopithecinae
sites at Sterkfontein.

2. "to complete excavations at the remarkable Makapan
site discovered by Dr. van Riet-Lowe. In this little African
Chou-Kou-Tien (. . .) there is a definite chance of finding the
bones of *early Pleistocene Man* in South Africa. One of my plans
is to visit the site this month."

3. "about a hundred miles from Capetown" an open site had
been found which was equivalent to that of Makapan but, "the
place has not yet been examined by competent stratigraphists."

The distribution of the various tasks to be performed was
made difficult by problems of conflicting personalities with

* P. Leroy, p. 44.        † See page 164.

the additional complication of political rivalries, but Teilhard's candour proved an effective diplomatic weapon and he was able to settle matters to everyone's satisfaction.

Never the sort of man to remain idle while others were working, Teilhard refused to rest on the laurels he had won at Chou-Kou-Tien. Unbound by *a priori* theories, he was able to modify his ideas in accordance with the facts. From September onwards, he found himself confronted by new problems of a palaeontological nature: they were:

The problem of the pebble industry—the oldest human industry.

The problem of the geographical origins of the first men— was the answer to be found in Kenya and Uganda? This last hypothesis (which has been revived by Dr. Leakey) was proposed by Teilhard to the South African Archaeological Society in the course of a lecture he gave on October 12: "In Europe and Asia, Man appears as a new-comer, but in this country he appears as an autochthonous being. Such is the great lesson learnt in a visit to South Africa by a geologist and palaeontologist of Asia."*

As always, contact with the earth had a reinvigorating effect on Teilhard's mind: "This contact with the terrain has excited me and made me feel younger" (September 16, 1951).

One can, of course, come to the definite conclusion that his Roman superiors were nothing but systematic persecutors, lacking in any good will towards him, but to the unprejudiced mind it should be possible to understand why they were so glad to see Teilhard go back to his work in the field, and why there was to be a *détente* in their relations with him: they were happy to have put the Father back on what they considered to be the *right path for him.*

As if to make up for lost time, Teilhard decided to visit South America after South Africa for the purposes of his synthesis. This rapid visit in the last ten days of October 1951 was unfortunately confined to seeing collections and museums and, as he said himself, "the analogies and contrasts between the two continents came to him as a shock" (November 8, 1951). A new problem had arisen which was to haunt his geologist's mind: what solution was there to the problem of the genesis of the continents?

* Analysis quoted by Cuénot, pp. 391-2.

At the end of November 1951, the expedition was over and Teilhard found himself "provisionally stranded or perched" at the Wenner-Gren Foundation in New York. In 1952 he devoted himself to careful, patient manoeuvring in order to ensure that both aid and financial assistance should be forthcoming from the Foundation for the work he had promoted in South Africa, for it was necessary to help the scientists who were already on the site. His diplomacy was successful for he was personally sent to Africa with a subsidy of five thousand dollars.

Makapan—"the little Chou-Kou-Tien"—began to be decisively excavated. In January 1953 a "skull-cap of a Man analogous to *Homo rhodiensis* was found to the north of Cape Town . . .; but it seems that it is of relatively recent date". Teilhard did not leave New York for South Africa until July 1. He also made a brief excursion to Northern Rhodesia with halts on the way there and back, both at Makapan and at Cape Town. Never imposing himself, and never stepping into anybody else's place, he inspired and directed researches everywhere. He promised himself that he would obtain subsidies from the Wenner-Gren Foundation for new excavations in the southern Sahara, and wished to link up his work with the research in progress in Portuguese Angola and the Nebada valley in India.

"All in all, I am as satisfied as it is possible to be with the results of my trip. I have learned and seen much, and I think my ideas are now clearer on the geological origins of the human race,* and I have the feeling that I have helped (with the Foundation's dollars) to establish a remarkable research network in South Africa and in the southern Sahara" (September 8, 1953).

The voyage only ended after Teilhard had made a second detour to South America, from the end of September 1953 until November 2 when he arrived back in New York.

To complete making the network he had set up fully effective, Teilhard planned a trip to France and England in order to "contact the key-scientists", Arambourg, Mortelmans, and Oakley. The result was a trip to Paris and London in 1954,

* "L'Afrique et les origines humaines", *Revue des questions scientifiques*, 1955, no. 1.

with the permission of his superiors at Rome. It was a lightning
trip which only lasted for two months. From June 9 to August 5
he was in Paris where he lectured to learned societies, and in
Lyon where he saw the Provincial head of the Order. From
August 6 to the 10th he was in London. "With new restrictions
imposed upon him, broken by an emotion he could scarcely
contain, and torn by horrible anguish, he cut short his stay in
Paris and returned to New York six weeks earlier than antici-
pated."* At the end of this last trip to Europe, when the
moment came to say farewell, Doctor René Loriot realised how
painful it was for Teilhard to leave again: "His distress was
pitiful to see, and we rapidly separated." Once back in New
York, "Teilhard still suffered from terrible feelings of desolation
and longings to see France again, if only for a few moments."†

Nevertheless, when Father Leroy saw him a few days before
Christmas 1954, he found him "somewhat more tranquil".‡

A new refusal from his superiors must have been painful for
him: "received a letter from Father X . . . extremely friendly
but advising me not to ask to come to the meeting at the Sorbonne in April (Palaeontology)—meeting to which Piveteau
and the Recherche Scientifique invited me" (March 1, 1955).

There was no complaint. His renunciation of the dearest
thing in life to him—the diffusion of his ideas—was complete.
His attachment to the mystical love of Christ was absolute:
"In the meantime, the only thing to do is to follow the line of
conduct that has been tried a hundred times over: to go on
fighting, without bitterness and with an immense *inner* confidence.—Nothing can withstand an ever-increasing love of the
'Christic phylum' " (March 14, 1955). Only such a love could
root out self-love: "to a friend who was telling him of her
recent trials and their effect on her spirit", Teilhard replied, "I
can no longer look at myself."§

During a dinner at the French Consulate on March 15,
Teilhard declared in the presence of his nephews: "I should
like to die on the day of the Resurrection." This desire was
inspired by his faith in the Universal Presence of the resuscitated Christ, as this prayer of his makes clear.**

* Leroy, pp. 45-6.     † Cuénot, p. 445.
‡ Leroy, p. 46.        § *Nouvelles lettres de voyages*, p. 14.
** Quoted by Cuénot, p. 469, without reference; Cf. Leroy, p. 65.

"Lord, since with every instinct and throughout all the changing fortunes of my life, I have never ceased to search for you and to set you at the heart of universal matter, it will be in the resplendence that shines through all things and which lights up the universe that I shall have the joy of closing my eyes."

On April 2, he confided in Father Gannon, his Rector at New York, "with such spontaneity and charm that I thought I saw a child before me".

On Holy Saturday, he made his confession to his friend, the French Jesuit Father de Breuvery.

On Easter Sunday, April 10, 1955, he went to High Mass at Saint Patrick's Cathedral after having said mass himself.

That evening, as he returned from a concert to have tea with friends, he fell down and fainted. When he came to he said, "I don't remember anything; this time it's terrible." The doctor who was sent for urgently, could only confirm the seriousness of his state and advised that a priest be called. When a priest from the New York Jesuits' Residence arrived, Pierre Teilhard de Chardin had just died. He was seventy-four years old.

After a simple low mass, he was buried in the presence of some ten witnesses in foreign soil, on April 12, at nine o'clock in the morning.

**2**

---

## *Contrasts of Personality*

### THE MAN OF THE EARTH AND THE MAN OF HEAVEN

A SIX-YEAR-OLD boy was walking along the road towards the mountains of Auvergne, hand-in-hand with a four-year-old little girl. They had, as a matter of fact, been forbidden to go beyond the limits of the château of Sarcenat where they were living. As Claude Aragonnès has related, "It was with some anxiety that a search was made for them. Where could they have got to?" The two children had already gone a considerable way on the road towards the mountains when they were caught. "What were you going to do?" they were asked. "See what is inside the volcanoes!" answered Pierre, thus beginning his career as an explorer-geologist at the age of six.*

This anecdote has an even more symbolical significance when we consider what fate had in store for the little girl. Two years younger than Pierre, she was his favourite sister: "We understood each other completely without need of explanations, even in the way we behaved and reacted to events throughout our lives."† At the age of twenty she was to be confined to her bed by an attack of Pott's disease, and she was never to leave it. But far from admitting defeat from her illness, she turned it to a greater purpose, by joining the Union catholique des malades and becoming its president from 1927 to 1936. She served it

---

* *L'Auvergne littéraire*, 3rd trimester, 1957, p. 12.

† *"Témoignage fraternel"*, *Le Trait d'Union*, Union catholique des malades, no. 66, October 1936, p. 6.

with an energy that earned her the nick-name of the "Maré-chale", and inspired the sub-title of a pamphlet devoted to her, written by Monique Givelet—*L'énergie spirituelle de la souffrance.**

Another of Pierre's sisters, Françoise, was also destined to bear the stigmata of Sacrifice. After a long period of spiritual trial, she gave up everything to devote herself to the poor, and became a "little sister of the Poor". She went to Shanghai where she became Mother Superior, caught smallpox and died at the age of thirty-two, leaving her bones in the same far-off country where her brother was to discover the bones of Early Man.

For a long time Pierre wondered whether he would have to make the choice between the Earth, which attracted him with its promise of giving him the joy of "discovering what it had within it . . .", and Heaven where two of his sisters had entered through the narrow gate of suffering and renunciation. When he had reconciled his two opposing inclinations, he had not only resolved his spiritual crisis at the age of twenty: he had also formulated the guiding principle for his inner, apostolic life, both in theory and in practice, both for himself and for others.

The crisis came in Jersey during his early training period with the Jesuits: "There was a struggle in the very depths of my soul between the God of on-High and a sort of new God of Onward, due to the definitive coexistence and unbreakable reconciliation in my heart of the cosmic Sense and the Christic Sense.

"I find the first signs of this opposition in my years at college, in my pathetic attempts to reconcile my yearning towards Nature with the (certainly too narrow) evangelism of the Imitation of Jesus Christ which inspired my morning prayers. Later, when I was a novice in Jersey, I was seriously considering a total renunciation of the science of stones . . . in order to give myself completely to so-called 'supernatural' activities. I owe the fact that I had not 'gone off the rails' at that time to the robust common sense of Father T(roussard) (master of the novices). As a matter of fact, Father Troussard confined himself at the time to declaring that the God of the Cross was

* Marguerite-Marie Teilhard de Chardin, *L'énergie spirituelle de la souf-france*, Paris, Editions Le Seuil, 1951.

expecting the 'natural' expansion of my being as well as its sanctification, without telling me why or how. But this was enough to allow me to keep the two threads in my hands, and I found myself saved from the crisis."*

The practical solution to the problem, a solution acquired from that very moment, was, therefore, the decision taken through obedience to his superior, to follow the road of Science and the road leading to Perfection at one and the same time.

The theoretical solution to the problem still had to be formulated clearly. Teilhard was to spend his life in endeavours to clarify his view of the solution and to live according to it.

In 1917, while he was still a soldier, Pierre Teilhard gave the title of *Le milieu mystique* to a work of forty-three pages he had written.†

The *Milieu Divin* appeared in its first edition at Tien-Tsin in 1926-7.‡ But as early as 1925 Teilhard had "tried out" its contents on some pupils of the École Normale who had asked him for a retreat of three days on Shrove Tuesday: "Far from being a peripheral province of Christian activity, far from having to justify itself as being a concession made to our weakness by the Church, human activities and the work of the World were shown to us as the most direct expression, and the extension of the central will of God with regard to the World. Its relation to the most demanding inner life and the greatest personal love for Jesus Christ, came to several of us and to myself as a definite revelation."§

One of the most complete definitions that Teilhard ever gave to the practical and theoretical solution to the problem which haunted him during his whole life is doubtless to be found in this extract from *How I believe (Comment je crois)*:**

"The originality of my belief lies in the fact that it is rooted in two spheres of life which are usually considered as mutually antagonistic. By my education and intellectual training I belong to the 'children of heaven'. But by temperament and

---

* *Le Cœur de la Matière*, quoted by Viallet in *L'Univers personnel de Teilhard de Chardin*, pp. 39 sq.
† No. 18 in the Cuénot bibliography.
‡ No. 85 in the Cuénot bibliography.
§ Jacques Perret, a Professor at the Sorbonne, quoted by Cuénot, p. 83.
** Quoted by Tresmontant, *Introduction à la pensée de Teilhard de Chardin*, p. 101. The work is dated 1934, cf. the Cuénot bibliography, no. 157.

professional training I am a 'child of the Earth'. Thus set by life at the centre of two worlds, whose theory, language and emotions I knew from familiar experience, I set up no internal barriers. But I gave two apparently contradictory influences full freedom to play on each other. Now, at the end of this process, after having spent thirty years in seeking for inner unity, I have the impression that a synthesis has been reached between the two poles that attracted me. One has never killed the other. Today I probably believe more than ever in God, and certainly more than ever in the World."

This was written in 1934.

In 1950, at the time he was revising *Le Cœur de la Matière*,* Teilhard confessed that he had not "finished trying to work out what the risks are for someone whose inner law and necessity compels him to leave the well-tried but henceforth under-humanised path of a certain type of traditional asceticism in order to seek a way towards Heaven (not a middle way but a synthetic way) in which the entire dynamism of Matter and the Flesh merges with the genesis of the Spirit." He goes on: "He who does this will sometimes find himself afraid (without being able to restrain himself) by the novelty, the daring, and at the same time the paradoxical possibility of the attitudes he finds himself, both intellectually and emotionally, obliged to assume, if he wishes to remain faithful to his fundamental purpose: that of reaching Heaven by encompassing the Earth."

### FROM THE GOD OF IRON TO THE GOD OF SPIRIT

"As far back as I can remember (before I was six years old) I find existing in myself a *strictly* dominating passion: the passion for the Absolute.

"Evidently, I had not yet given a name to the disquiet that had assailed me—but, today, I can recognise it without any hesitation whatever.

"From my childhood the need to completely possess 'some Absolute' was the axis of my inner life. Among all the pleasure of this period, I was only happy (I remember perfectly clearly) *in relation* to a fundamental joy which generally came from the possession (or the thought) of some more precious, rare, consistent and unalterable object. Sometimes it might be some

* No. 302 of the Cuénot bibliography. Quoted by Viallet, p. 41.

piece of metal. Sometimes, leaping to the other extreme, I took pleasure in the thought of the God-Spirit (the Flesh of Our Lord then seemed to me something too fragile and too corruptible).

"Such preoccupations might seem to be strange. I repeat it was always the same, without a break. From that time I felt the invincible (but yet vivifying and calming) need to find peace *without interruption* in something tangible and definite;—and I looked everywhere for this beatifying object.

"The story of my inner life is that of this search, bearing on increasingly universal and perfect realities. At bottom, my innermost natural tendency—the *nisus* of my soul has remained absolutely inflexible as long as I can remember myself."*

We find a kind of religious psychology that is seldom encountered . . . or confessed, in his fragment of *Mon Univers*, as well as in the autobiographical passages in the *Cœur de la Matière*. A hasty reader who wished to express himself in approximative terms would be tempted to say that the young Teilhard was a spontaneous materialist and pantheist, and an unconscious follower of a Stoic type of thought. Teilhard even lays himself open to this charge: the "beloved friend" to whom he gave voice in a work entitled *Le Christ dans la Matière* confesses, "I have always had a naturally pantheistic soul."

It may be conceded that many of Teilhard's expressions are confused, ambiguous, and liable to be taken as the professions of faith of a true materialist pantheist if taken out of their context.

But these formulas which would be inadmissible coming from a Christian and a priest are always surrounded and modified by others which clearly define the sole object of his adoration. The beginnings of pantheism or materialism are always impregnated with the atmosphere of an Absolute which admits of no ambiguity and which escapes from the inhibiting deficiencies of Matter left to itself.

What always passionately interested Teilhard, both in his youth and in his old age, was never Matter itself but the Absolute in Matter. That is to say, something he found in the

* *Mon Univers*, 1918, reproduced in facsimile by Cuénot facing p. 75; reproduced in the roneo copy of *Le Cœur de la Matière* (Bibliotheque nationale. Res. M.R. 142), p. 3, note 1.

heart of matter which completely escaped from the lamentable decay to which all fragments of matter are disappointingly prone. He was looking for the imperishable, but everything around him was destined to perish: iron is hard but it rusts; diamonds never scratch but they break; a flame is unassailable but it can be extinguished. Where then does Permanence reside?

This, then was the problem lying at the heart of all metaphysics and religions, the problem that faced all the great religious thinkers. But the paths they took to seek its solution were liable to vary greatly.

Struck and even wounded by the mutability of all terrestrial things, St. Augustine looked for peace to God, the Immutable. But how was God to be conceived? Like Teilhard, he first saw him in Matter, and in the guise of Matter itself: "Lord my God, O Truth, I considered you as a luminous and immense body, and myself as a fragment of this body . . . O excessive perversity! Such, though, was my attitude!"—"It was impossible for me to imagine any other substance than that which I could see with my eyes."—"I conceived of You as an immense being, penetrating the whole mass of the universe from all sides through infinite spaces, and going beyond the universe to stream out into the infinite, so that the earth contained You within itself, as did the sky, and as did all things, and that everything found its limits within You, while you remained limitless. But just as this mass of air, this air above the earth, does not stop the passage of the sun's rays, and does not stop them from penetrating it, and crossing through it without breaking or tearing it, and is filled entirely by this light, so I thought that the mass of the sky, of the air, of the sea, of the earth itself could be suffused by You, and let itself in its smallest and largest parts be penetrated by You, and embraced by your presence; and thus, be it within or be it without, your mysterious breath would have sway over all that You have created."

But, if St. Augustine had indeed given way to the temptations of Matter, was this not partly due to the fact that he had surrendered to the attractions of carnal passions and the Manichean heresy?

This was certainly not the case with Teilhard who was "saved" thanks to his exemplary family.

Thérèse Martin of the Infant Christ, another extraordinarily precocious child, also had a very early experience in life of the fragility of earthly things: "Before leaving, I took out the snack that I had brought in my little basket. Alas! The beautiful slice of bread and jam that my sisters had prepared for me had changed its appearance. Instead of its former bright colour all I saw was a light pink tint, *all aged and shrunken*. Then the earth seemed an even sadder place than before to me, and I understood that only in Heaven would joy remain unclouded."*

In Teilhard's family, as in the Martin family, there had been talk of heaven. But whereas Thérèse turned away from the Earth for ever to fix her gaze on Heaven, after her first experience of the corruptible and perishable nature of earthly things, Pierre went on searching for what he had not found at first. The passion for the Absolute had led Thérèse to suddenly install herself, for the rest of her life, in the midst of this Absolute, once it had been revealed to her. The same passion encouraged Pierre to never again despise this fragile Matter which had both revealed and symbolised the true Absolute to him. Obscurely and instinctively, he felt that Iron, Quartz, and the Flame all had a profound affinity with the Spirit. And the Heaven in which he believed, since he trusted his mentors, could not make him renounce that reflection of heaven he had seen shining at the heart of metals and minerals . . . All his life, the Man of Heaven and the Man of Earth within him would illumine each other, instead of fighting to the death. The worshipper of Iron was soon to find out that what he was worshipping was not Iron, nor any other comparable substance. But the worshipper of the God of pure Spirit was always to find out that Man has no other means of reaching Heaven save by way of the Earth; for this is the attestation and the proclamation by every smallest particle of matter, that the Being is, and that He is imperishable, definitive and absolute.

From this point of view then, the profound religious psychology of Pierre Teilhard de Chardin appears irreducible and strangely original. By temperament a materialist-pantheist, it was the realisation of this fundamental inclination in himself which was to give added effect to his lessons in the Faith, by opening his eyes to their true profundity, their gravity and their

* *Histoire d'une âme*, chapter II.

reality. For many Christians catechism is imposed on an intelligence that never really appreciates it, because it has never experienced the need for it. For Teilhard, catechism was the key to a mystery he had already felt: that unknown God worshipped by the child in the guise of a lump of metal or stone was now felt to be an immense Spirit which could yet be incarnated in the flesh of Man. . . .

Not everything, then, was wrong in his childish pantheism: God-the-Spirit can be at the heart of Matter, and the Resurrection of the Flesh where God is incarnated sets it at the heart of all Matter. . . .

It must be admitted that this last discovery took some time for the young Pierre certainly loved Jesus, under the influence of his mother, but "his true self was elsewhere. . . ."

Then came the day when worship of the Sacred Heart, completely authorised and recommended by the Church, gave him a synthetic symbol in which he could go beyond adoration of matter as corruptible as "human flesh":

"For me . . . to see a mysterious purple and gold stain taking shape in the very centre of the chest of the Saviour, this was, from the very first instant, the means of *escaping* at last from everything that had hurt me so much in the complicated and fragile organisation of the body of Jesus! Astonishing liberation! It was not by any purely physical means but rather by a process of convergence and concentration that the whole physical and spiritual reality of Christ manifested itself to me in a clearly defined and compact object in which all accidental and limiting particularities had vanished away. This was the first approximation of a Christic vision going beyond Christ, and a strange homology between this new 'milieu' and the Metal or Mineral which still held sway in me at the same time— on the other side, still running through my soul."*

The youthful worshipper of the God of Iron, soon to become a worshipper of the God of Spirit, did not give up his childhood dream: he found the absolute, and thus the adorable, in the innermost depths of universal reality. He conceived of this innermost depth as something that united matter as he had dreamed of it, together with spirit as he had wished it. At a certain point the dogma of the Incarnation offered him this

* *Le Cœur de la Matière*, quoted by Viallet, p. 42.

twin reality that his heart and soul longed for: a reality that consisted of living matter that was yet immortal, since it had been resuscitated, and which was at the same time absolute but still personal spirit. Christ, the Sacred Heart, the Victor of Death on Easter Morning, the ruler of the Worlds on the eve of Ascension—such was the solution to Teilhard's problem as a child. The only difference was that his adult intelligence would place this Sacred Heart at the centre of an unbreakable structure of a physical, moral, mystical and universal law—the "law of Convergence" or "Complexification" which brought all things together in a Centre of Unity through Love. Such would be Teilhard's personal religious conviction, in which it seemed the most natural thing in the world that the most modern science should go hand in hand with the most traditional religious doctrine. But the solution still essentially depended on the person of the God Incarnate.

In 1940, when the war had kept him away from his *Laboratory for researches into continental geology* (Laboratoire pour les recherches de geologie continentale), and Teilhard founded the *Institute for Geo-biology* (*Institut de Géobiologie*) at Peking, it was only natural that this institute should be dedicated to Christ the King. At the entrance to the building was written a motto taken from Saint Paul: "*Ut sit Deus omnia in omnibus*—May God be everything in all things."*

In Teilhard's eyes, Christ represented that privileged (crucial) point in the universe which is the meeting-place between Spirit and Matter, so that worshipping Christ one is certain to be worshipping God, both in spirit and in reality, while still being justified in worshipping Matter which has become literally God-like.

### THE INDIFFERENT DISCIPLE

Henri Brémond never forgot the astonishment he experienced during his years as a teacher at the College at Mongré when he met a boy who was head of the class but who never showed the slightest emotion: "Thirty years ago, when I was teaching the humanities, I had a little Auvergnat in my class, who was very intelligent, always came first, but who was desperately well-behaved. Even the stubbornest and dullest boys livened up

* I Corinthians, 15. 28.

sometimes when a more exciting reading or a more interesting subject brought a light to their eyes. But he—never. It was only a long time afterwards that I learned the secret reason for this apparent indifference. He had another passion, a jealous, absorbing passion, that made him live in a different world from ours: he was in love with stones."*

We now know that it was not just stones, properly speaking, that excited him: more than Iron or Quartz they were the God-Spirit to him, the Heart of Christ beating in the heart of the Universe.

This is why, when Brémond writes that he lived "in a different world from ours", he does not simply mean that Teilhard was "indifferent to the charms of literature"† but rather that he had withdrawn into himself, as if into a kind of perpetual inner retreat, to the very centre of his being where a flame burnt that none had lit and that none could put out.

It was not that Pierre Teilhard was reserved. On the contrary, he avidly asked questions to learn what it was indispensable for him to know: after all, was he not head of the class, the kind of pupil who trusts in his teachers, who shows interest, who listens, and who absorbs what he hears?

There was, however, one thing that he did not need to learn from anyone, because it was always burning in his consciousness, and which he could show to no-one because it was too private to display—his passionate enthusiasm for the only thing in the world which merited it.

Now that we have followed the course of his life, we see that Teilhard's attitude towards his "teachers", were they his parents, his Church, or the scientists and philosophers to whom he listened most willingly, was never to change. Thanks to the fullness of a passion that drew its substance from everything and which never changed, Pierre Teilhard saw everything, listened to everything, studied everything; he was able to benefit from every contact and experience. But, like an organism or a flame that transforms everything that feeds it into its own substance, Teilhard was to transmute every lesson, idea and emotion in order to assimilate them in the great synthesis that had been growing within him ever since his childhood.

* Henri Brémond, *Le Charme d'Athènes*, p. 29.
† See *L'Œuvre du P. Teilhard de Chardin, Études*, July-August 1950, p. 126.

Let us turn to his spiritual autobiography again:* at the age of six or seven he was "affectionate, *well-behaved* (the word Brémond had used to describe him: 'desperately well-behaved'), and even pious" . . . "But, in reality, *my true self was elsewhere.*—And to see it in the open, it would have been necessary to watch me when—*always secretly and without uttering a word*—I *withdrew* into the contemplation of my God, Iron, without even thinking that there *was anything to tell anyone* . . ."

I have italicised the words which seem to be characteristic: we see that the young Pierre withdrew into his secret, in order to devote himself to the only activity which interested him and which did not necessarily correspond to what his superiors were teaching him. His search for privacy was neither due to any feeling of shame, nor to any wish to dissimulate, but simply to the fact that there are some inclinations, needs and actions that are so far removed from all social life and so free from the necessity of outside encouragement that it would be ridiculous and even immodest to display them, or even talk about them.

It was this same secret worship of the Absolute that was to develop without any radical change as Teilhard became an adult, taking on an intellectual and apostolic form. What made for unity in his life was the permanence of an intuition that remained free from any exterior influence, and which progressively adapted itself as he matured and reached old age. There was no question of Teilhard's voluntarily withdrawing into himself, nor of an automatic reflex of self-preservation: Teilhard simply continued with his objective perception of a Reality which manifested itself in everything, despite everything, even if its aspect was to change during a lifetime of research and endeavour:

"A true process, biologically guided and guaranteed in my eyes by the identity which was clearly perceptible to my consciousness, of the psychological sub-stratum in question, throughout all its metamorphoses and enlargements."†

Teilhard grew to manhood. As a student he read Bergson, and as an adult he met Le Roy. *A priori*, it might be supposed that he was to learn much from contact with these two great minds. But, let us look a little closer:

"It was during my years of theology at Hastings (i.e. just

* *Le Cœur de la Matière*, p. 3.      † *Ibid.*, p. 2.

after the wonders of Egypt) that I felt myself filled by the consciousness of a profound, total, ontological, drift of the Universe around me, which, much less as an abstract notion than as a presence, grew in me little by little until it invaded my entire inner world.

"Under what influences, from what shock, by what process and what stages, did this feeling arise and root itself so deeply in my being? . . . I should be hard put to it to say. I remember that at the time I was avidly reading *Creative Evolution*. But, apart from the fact that at this time my understanding of Bergson's concept of Duration was rather limited, I can clearly see that the effect of these glowing pages on me was to stir up the fire that was already consuming my heart and soul at just the right moment, in a brief instant."

The confession seems clear enough. There was not one idea that Teilhard the disciple received from reading Bergson that he did not already have. It was not that Teilhard closed himself to communication from outside for he read "avidly" and was conscious of the excitement that the book aroused in him. But the second and most durable reaction of this young mind was to fall back on his own intuitions: he benefited from the contributions of others but remained steadfast in his own opinions.

Let it be well understood: we must not jump to the conclusion that Teilhard remained content to regard Bergson's work as merely being fuel for his own intellectual fire for this would be to reduce Teilhard's vision to the dimensions of an opinion. For, in his eyes, there was no question of his convictions being a personal theory invented by himself and for which he searched for proofs. It was not even a question of what Teilhard himself had called "the identity of a psychological sub-stratum" (a formula typical of the psychology of the end of the century). Rather it was a question of what he now called, with much greater insight, "a presence which invaded my inner world". It was not an abstract notion, not a thesis to be proved, not a system to be built up, but a presence. Bergson's book may well have encouraged Teilhard's ardent longing for this invading presence, but Bergson himself had nothing to do with the fact that Teilhard was conscious of it.

Similarly, the personal and intellectual friendship between Teilhard and Edouard Le Roy should have favoured every

kind of exchange between them. But when the two friends
describe their intellectual exchanges, they do so in rather a
different manner.

In his published lectures, Le Roy has often affirmed that it
was impossible to distinguish between his own contribution
and that of Teilhard's in the ideas he put forward: "We
would not be able to make an exact estimate of our respective
efforts",* and elsewhere he declares: "I have discussed the
views expressed above so often and for so long with Father
Teilhard that we ourselves can no longer define our respective
parts in their formation. I must, therefore, limit myself, in fact
I am practically obliged to do so, to quoting for the two of us,
once and for all."† Again he writes: "All I have done is to
summarise . . . an unpublished work by Father Teilhard, in
which he revealed the results of our meditations in common."‡

Quite different is the way Teilhard describes the debt he
owed to his great friend: "I loved him like a father, and owed
him much. It is not exactly a case of being indebted to him for
any particular idea, but, especially between 1920 and 1930, it
was he who gave me confidence, widened my spirit (and my
sense of loyalty to the Church . . .) and who also served (at the
Collège de France) as a tribune for my emerging ideas on
hominisation and the 'noosphere'. I think that the word
'noosphere' is my own (does one ever really know?) but it was
he who launched it" (December 3, 1954).

Teilhard confesses to owing much to Le Roy but when he
comes to details he acknowledges no new notions to his friend
and no allogeneous fertilisation. Le Roy helped him to be himself, giving him greater confidence, greater range, and a greater
audience as well. . . .

We must not construe Teilhard's attitude as being one of
egocentricism, pride, and a refusal to acknowledge a debt to
anyone, and blindness to the fact of his dependence on those
around him. Teilhard *did* recognise his dependence on others;
he proclaimed it and rejoiced in it, but it was his dependence
as a scientist that was in question. In what concerned his
deepest passion, the very mainspring of his life, he was beyond

* *Les Origines humaines et l'évolution de l'intelligence*, chap. I, p. 8.
† *L'Exigence idéaliste et le fait de l'Évolution*, p. 82, note 1.
‡ *Essai d'une philosophie première*, p. 413.

all outside intervention for the very simple reason that, in his eyes, it was not himself that mattered but a "Cause" that was infinitely more important.

Let us think of Teilhard as he was during the "Yellow Expedition". He was plunged into a milieu which was totally different from the scientific world he was accustomed to. Nevertheless he remained on an equal footing with all the others, he made friends, he never refused a discussion, and he never shrank from taking blows in an argument. The only thing he complained of was of never being able to "be alone" but in the following terms: "One of the weak points of this journey is the near-impossibility of 'solitary reflection' due to the number and the diversity of the members of the expedition. They are a very agreeable lot (although the compact group of mechanics represent a rather more heterogeneous mass than the rest), but one is never alone, either physically or mentally. I live identified with my work. My meditated, conscious reactions will doubtless follow later" (July 7, 1931).

By itself this letter proves nothing, except that, like everyone, except those with a cenobite's vocation (and even then—?) Teilhard felt the legitimate desire to collect his thoughts in solitude.

We may, however, find a symbolical significance in this picture of Teilhard utterly absorbed in his work, completely merged in a team of scientists and technicians who were otherwise completely different from him, both by education and convictions and only complaining of one thing—the impossibility of getting away on his own.

This picture will come to life and make sense if we read this revealing sentence concerning the anonymous fictitious hero (a spokesman for the author) in a story by Teilhard entitled *La Puissance spirituelle de la Matière*:

"He had found it—at last! A *support* and a resource *outside* Society!"

The man who was to take the idea of *team-work* so far on a world scale, and who conceived the theory of the unification of the human race in the Noosphere was, by one of History's many paradoxes, liable to be regarded as "a lonely man".

He might be described as a "solitary member of a team".

"Solitary?" If this is what he was, it was not through disdain for others, or from any disability, but only because of the exclusive nature of a passion which sundered all other links to its own advantage.

"I have the curious impression of having lost the faculty of taking pleasure in (or desiring) anything at all with regard to myself, while, at the same time, I am continually dominated by the supreme grandeur of the universal enterprise in which we are all engaged by the fact of our existence. It is a kind of impassioned indifference, in which all human interventions or ambitions are noticeably almost non-existent" (December 6, 1929).

"Indifference"; Teilhard was repeating the word Brémond chose for him, but without qualifying it by the adjective "apparent" . . .

"Impassioned"; he echoed the explanation given by Brémond, for his indifference was indeed due to a passion: an absorbing but secret passion which could be communicated but which could not be influenced by others, and which only showed itself on the outside by this "kind of indifference" to everything outside its sphere.

Father Teilhard seems to have been endowed to the highest degree with two apparently contradictory faculties, whose simultaneous development can be explained by his unique passion for the Absolute: on one hand he had the *faculty of communication* which, to a rare if not almost unique degree, allowed him to participate in expeditions and scientific collaboration in a sympathetic atmosphere generated by his almost irresistible personal charm; on the other hand, he had the *faculty of withdrawal* which almost always allowed him to retreat into his inner being, to steep himself again in the certitude of his inner convictions, and to endure silences, storms, criticisms, and interdictions . . . without ever deviating from the course he had chosen to follow.

### AN OBEDIENT BUT STUBBORN SON OF THE CHURCH

Teilhard was both one and the other; he was as obedient as only a Jesuit can be, and yet he was also as stubborn as only an Auvergnat can be. . . .

To be a Jesuit means that one is a member of the Church, the mystical body of Christ, and also a member of a religious society constituted as an Order. He therefore owes a twofold obedience. There can be little doubt that such a notion can hardly be understood by a non-believer, especially a non-believer of the present day at a time when generally accepted social philosophies would have us believe that obedience is the opposite of liberty.

Let it be said, once and for all, that to compare the obedience of a Christian to the authority of the Church with the passive obedience of members of a totalitarian society is to give a completely false picture of the situation. Whether he be a Jesuit or not, when a Catholic obeys the legitimate authority of the Church in matters where it is competent, he is not conscious of obeying a man, but only God. He knows that his submission is not for the benefit of any group of men, but for the common good of Humanity which is the same as the common good of the Universe.

Nevertheless, even when it speaks in the name of God and aims at the universal common good, the Church has no power to impose beliefs which are diametrically opposed to the believer's own convictions. When authority has decided on what should be believed, it does not arbitrarily give orders to the faithful but simply defines that which constitutes divine faith which God in his grace has accorded to every believer. The Catholic is, therefore, persuaded in advance (otherwise he would have lost his faith) that his Church, which was founded by Jesus and animated by His spirit, can neither add to nor subtract from the essentials of the Faith. In this domain of dogmatic truth it is a question of believing rather than obeying.

There is, however, another domain in which Authority can intervene: in matters concerning the Christian conscience which do not directly touch the essential dogmas, be they theoretical conceptions or practical decisions. This is where the element of obedience comes in, and it does not essentially differ in the Church from obedience in any other normally con-stituted society. The individual who thinks differently from his superiors is bound to make his thoughts and his reasons known to them. If the duly enlightened superiors maintain their decision, then the common good requires that the thoughts of the individual should give precedence to the thoughts of whoever is responsible for the preservation of the common good. Otherwise, actions taken under the pretext of doing good would only result in harm. But this submission does not prevent the individual from refusing to accept any unreasonable orders: if Authority ordered a sin to be committed or tried to impose itself in a domain that did not belong to it, the individual who had evidence of this would not be bound to obey.

This summary résumé is necessary if we are to understand Teilhard's attitude towards authority. All his behaviour, in fact, shows that his Faith and his submission remained intact and undiminished.

On one hand, he believed everything that the Church would have us believe, and only that; he never considered that his own vision of things was in the nature of a new Revelation superseding the traditional Revelation, for he only thought that the way in which he put forward his views was, henceforth, the only way of winning over the most aware and thoughtful minds of our time. Witness the work entitled "*The Heart of the Problem*" (*Le Cœur du Problème*), dated September 8, 1949, which he sent that same year to the Father Assistant who was the French *chargé d'affaires* at the headquarters of the General of the Order:

"(. . .) In these few pages, destined for the use of those better placed than myself, who are responsible for the direct or indirect guidance of the Church, I would like to make a frank exposition of where, in my opinion, the cause of the *malaise* from which we suffer lies, and of *how*, by a simple readjustment of this well located point, there is every chance of achieving a complete revival in a short time in the religious and Christian evolution of Humanity around us.

"Frankly", I say. "I am not preaching—that would be presumptuous. Still less am I criticising—that would be out of place. But, I am simply giving evidence from my life—an evidence that I am all the more unable to hush up as I am one of the few people in a position to give it."

Taken on its own, Faith in the World is not enough to impel the Earth onwards. But, taken in its turn, on its own, is it certain that the Christian Faith, in its ancient terms, is still enough to lift the World upwards?

". . . By definition, by principle, the distinguishing function of the Church is to know and to be able to Christianise all the

Pierre Teilhard de Chardin
aged two

Teilhard de Chardin
aged thirteen

Teilhard's family home at Sarcenat (Puy-de-Dome)

ABOVE, *left*: Teilhard de Chardin as a young Jesuit. ABOVE, *right*: Teilhard de Chardin in uniform during the the 1914-18 War.

LEFT: Teilhard de Chardin during the Yellow Expedition.

*Human element* in Man. Now, what is likely to happen (if it is not already happening . . .) if, at the precise moment when one more component begins to manifest itself in the *anima naturaliter christiana* with all the vivacity of the consciousness of a terrestrial 'ultra-human', ecclesiastical authority were to ignore, disdain or even condemn the new aspiration without succeeding in understanding it? This would be the result—neither more nor less: according as Christianity ceases (as it must do) to encompass the whole of the Human on earth, so it must lose its mordant vitality and the full bloom of its attraction. Because once it is under-humanised it will no longer give complete satisfaction to the faithful. It will no longer be so contagious for the non-believers. It will no longer be so resistant against its adversaries. It is being asked why there is so much spiritual disquiet in the hearts of the faithful and the clergy. Why are there so few deeply felt conversions in China despite the flocks of missionaries that have been sent there? Why is the Church so incapable (despite its welfare work and its devotion) of winning over the working masses? . . . My answer is simply that the magnificent Christian charity is lacking something at the present moment that would make it 'definitively active': that sensitivising dose of *human* faith and hope without which any religion—both *de jure* and *de facto*—can only appear as something stale, cold and unassimilable to Man."*

The man who wrote this was not a rebel. He was claiming neither to add nor to subtract from the dogma, but only that a new element and a new aspiration had emerged in Man, which needed to be transfigured by the traditional, integral Christian faith. Teilhard had not the slightest intention of substituting himself for established authority—on the contrary, he believed it was his duty to warn, to sound the alarm, and to enlighten. He would not have taken such pains if he had no longer respected authority or decided to no longer obey it.

But it is useless to hide the fact that neither the authorities in the Church nor in his Order ever agreed with him. They never failed to feel and to make known to Teilhard that his new presentation of the traditional faith was too open to debate, having insufficient basis and being badly formulated, for it to be safe to air it in public.

* *Le Cœur du Problème*, in *L'Avenir de l'Homme*, pp. 339-40 and 344-5.

C

How did Teilhard react to this reception of his views?

By obeying: he obeyed when his teaching post at the Institut Catholique was taken away from him, when he was repeatedly refused permission to publish, when he was advised not to accept any official post at Paris, when he was forbidden to write on philosophical and theological subjects, and when he was obliged to leave Paris to settle permanently in the United States. . . . He obeyed, not without some suffering, and even some moments of crisis, but all the same he obeyed, without undergoing any deep and long lasting disturbance.

"None the less, the fact remains that, with the stubbornness of an Auvergnat and above all due to his priestly vocation, he did all he could to get himself printed in order to win souls over to Christ."*

This was indeed the truth. He was unshakeably stubborn in the realisation of an ambition that had nothing earthly in its nature. He did not only try to "get himself printed", for the time came when he realised he could no longer be sure of that, but he endeavoured something which was even more important and which was to ensure the circulation of his ideas.

All means were good to this end—means permitted to him that is, since he was not allowed to print his writings he had them duplicated (from 1935 onwards); since he could not change the decision of Authority he tried, at least, to enlighten a subordinate who was well enough placed to be able to make his "cry" heard in high places ("it is this cry, and this cry alone, that he would like to hear here", *Le Cœur du Problème*); when, as in 1951, there was a risk of measures being taken against him which would have resulted in the destruction of his work due to the commotion his views had aroused, he effaced himself for a time; when, on the contrary, an honorary post was likely to give him a platform and to make his "shafts" more "penetrating", he accepted membership of the Institut de France.

If he finally resigned himself to the fact that he could not be printed he had a reason for it:

"I notice an increasing tendency for the keen edge of my thought to show itself outside my written essays, either at random or else during the excitement of writing letters to such and such a correspondent" (end of March (?) 1955).

* Cuénot, p. 323.

. . . Moreover, is it an offence to the memory of Father Teilhard to suggest that he may well have realised that the interdiction on his non-scientific writings constituted a sort of publicity-in-reverse for them? From several points of view, might it not have been to the advantage of a thought that had so little in common with fashionable philosophies for it not to be set down, black on white, in books that are easily bought, read and then shut again? There was a perpetual stimulus for him to go on always improving the way he formulated his intuitions, and also for his readers to never miss a single line that escaped from his pen. . . .

Claude Cuénot gets even nearer the mark when he writes: "He would have liked to see his influence freely at work and clearly revealed. But now he had found a real beatitude in the consciousness of working in obscurity, and with a supreme gesture of adoration, he respected the puzzling delays of the Master of the Universe and agreed to disappear and submit."*

Thus, without ever disobeying, he achieved his life-long desire.

And thus, the implacable words spoken by the narrator in the *Puissance spirituelle de la Matière* after recognising that "alone (Matter) and in its entirety, it would henceforth be his father, his mother, his family, race, and unique and burning passion" were to come true in the case of Teilhard's own life:

"And there were none who could gainsay him."

### FAITH IN GOD AND FAITH IN THE WORLD

The World! In Christian language, ever since the time of St. John, it has represented the antithesis to the Kingdom of Jesus: Jesus did not pray for the World, he vanquished the World; the World is Threefold Envy. One must choose between Christ and the World. The World is both a conglomeration of souls and an association of men who, under the rule of the Prince of this World, attach themselves to all that is visible, touchable and corporeal in order to idolise it.

If this is the case then is not the visible World something intrinsically bad, and to be condemned for ever? No, for God so loved the World that he sent his only Son, not to condemn it but to save it. . . .

* Cuénot, p. 265.

By this, it is evident that the word "World", *Kosmos*, is ambiguous. It can be used to designate both that excellent thing that God created, loved, and saved by incarnating himself in it, and that wretched reality that unbridled envy tends to make us prefer to God himself.

Through his deeper sensitivity, Pierre Teilhard was destined to suffer more than others from this contradiction lying at the very heart of the reality in which we are immersed. The only way he could escape from the dilemma was by taking his stand at the crucial point of divergence between the directions taken by the worldly on one hand, and the Christians on the other: the point where the World can be made divine. There are two ways of making the World divine: one is to make a God of it to be worshipped, the other is to see the presence of God in it, and to adore him in this *divine milieu* which he has arranged for our encounter with him and his Incarnation.

It was clearly the second way that Teilhard chose. Having renounced the Threefold Envy he could adore a Divine Presence in the World without danger to himself, and discern in it, as the quotation says that he placed at the head of *Le Cœur de la Matière*:

> At the heart of Matter
> A heart of the World,
> The heart of God.
> (*Au cœur de la Matière,*
> *Un Cœur du Monde,*
> *Le Cœur d'un Dieu.*)

What constitutes the paradox in Teilhard's life for us, with little knowledge of science and tepid faith, is that he should have been able to transform this Faith in God present in the World into a sort of *mystique* of the World as bearer of God.

This process had begun very early and went on gaining in depth: "(. . .) starting from when the first spark was lit— congenitally in me—throughout my whole life, during every moment of it, the World has been gradually lighting up and blazing before my eyes until it has come to surround me, entirely lit up from within . . ."*

What should be well understood is that there was a

* *Le Cœur de la Matière.*

co-existence (and perhaps even an identity) in Teilhard between intelligible aspiration and intuitive aspiration. He proclaimed his "insatiable need to maintain contact (*a contact through communion*) with a kind of universal root or matrix of living beings . . ." and he went on to add: "In fact, even when I reached the highest point in my spiritual trajectory, I only feel at ease when I am immersed in an ocean of Matter . . ."

Let there be no mistake, Teilhard never loved Matter for its own sake but only for the purpose it was serving: "Since instead of the spiritual fervour and the sublime purity of your saints, you have given me, my God, a feeling of irresistible sympathy for all that moves in the darkness of matter—and because I recognise myself to be irremediably a Son of the Earth rather than a Child of Heaven—in my thoughts this morning I will go up into the High Places bearing the hopes and the sufferings of my Mother, and there—strengthened by a priesthood which comes, I think, from you alone—I will call down Fire to touch all that is about to be born from human Flesh and to perish under the rising sun."*

That which moves in the heart of Matter, which is born in the Flesh and dies in the Flesh, all this was only a point of departure for Teilhard, but it was not enough to satisfy his aspirations. The World that passionately interested Teilhard was a World in which God showed himself at work, a World which was also to need the work of God.

Therefore, he asked God to lower his powerful, all-seeing, omnipresent hands:

"With your invincible hands, prepare the effort of the world through a supreme adaptation, for the great work you have in mind. (. . .) Reshape this effort, correct it, recast it, even in its origins, you who know why it is impossible for a creature to be born otherwise than as part of the stem of an un-ending Tree of Life."†

He asked God to declare, "This is my Body" over all life that germinates, grows up, blossoms and dies, and "This is my blood" over all things that die.

Was the World not consecrated then, by virtue of this prayer?

"In the new humanity that is being engendered today, the

* *La Messe sur le Monde.*        † Ibid.

Word has prolonged the never-ending act of its birth, and being immersed in the heart of the world, the great waters of Matter have become charged with life, although they do not move. In appearance nothing has stirred during the ineffable transformation, and yet, the immense Host of the Universe has, mysteriously and truly, become Flesh through contact with the substantial Word. All matter is henceforth incarnated, O my Lord, in your Incarnation."

We have now come to the most delicate, fascinating, and certainly the most obscure point in Teilhard's mystique of the World. Not the pagan, deified and idolised World but Christianised and even Christified World—to be sure. But—and this is the crucial question—to what extent do Teilhard's expressions overreach their mark? Was he speaking in metaphors or in precise terms?

Already, in his *Le Christ dans la matière*,* Teilhard spoke through the mouth of a friend (who resembled him like a brother) "who drank from the waters of life as one drinks from a holy source" and "whose soul instinctively communed with the Unique Life of things". The "well-beloved friend" asked himself: "Supposing that Christ were to deign to make a physical appearance before me—what would his aspect be? (. . .) Above all, in what manner would he make his noticeable apparition in matter? And what would his relation be to objects around him?" The answer to this question lay in a vision of Christ and his Heart offering himself to Mankind that progressively melted into its surroundings:

"One might say that the exterior appearances separating Christ from the world around Him had changed into a shimmering haze in which everything merged into one." Only an image, to be sure, but how exact did Teilhard intend it to be?

Seven years later, when he wrote *La Messe sur le Monde*,† were such images still sufficient for his purpose?

"In all the age-old inheritance of suffering and hope, no nostalgia can be greater than that which makes Man weep from frustration and desire in the heart of that anonymous and impalpable Presence which pervades all things around him: *Si forte attrectent eum.*"

---

* Written on the eve of the attack at Douaumont, October 1916.
† Ordos, Easter 1923. Cf. Cuénot bibliography, no. 53.

Can the prayer that arises out of such a nostalgia still nourish itself with images?

"O Lord, shatter the timidity of a puerile thought by the boldness of your Revelation (. . .). You, Jesus-Christ, 'in whom all things find their stability', reveal Yourself at last to those who love You, as the supreme Soul and physical source of Creation."

Christ, soul of the World! If such a formula is more and better than any image, it should be carefully explained. At least it gives us the key to Teilhard's faith and his innermost convictions: since the World is animated by Christ, then to have Faith in the World can only strengthen and extend Faith in God rather than contradicting it. This is what we should now realise from what we have learned of Teilhard's attitude.

As a result of living among laymen, a Christian may end up by becoming secular in his behaviour. Granted that he may keep his faith, but he may gradually lose the habit of reacting to his faith. His judgments, utterances and gestures will become modelled on those of the people around him. In the end he will assume a kind of double personality: on one hand his faith will follow its logical, practical course when he is alone to meditate and gather his thoughts, and on the other hand, in moments of weakness, he will assume a pose of thinking like everyone else rather than run the risk of offending the susceptibilities of others.

This was far from being the case with Teilhard. The absolute of his faith, or, as we may put it, faith in the Absolute, reinforced by his stubborn Auvergnat tenacity of mind, and, above all, strengthened by his meditations, saved him from this false double attitude.

When, on the orders of his superiors, Teilhard found himself plunged into the midst of a secular scientific and technical world, the result was quite unexpected and remarkable: far from his spirit being torn between two opposing extremes, it welcomed two worlds which seemed contradictory but which he accepted as being complementary.

Thanks to his talent for communication, Teilhard was able to understand the lay mind, but his gift of inner withdrawal saved him from being contaminated by it. He suffered from it, as a worshipper suffers among those who deny and despise the object of his worship. And yet he could not help feeling that he was a member of this world which believed itself to be "without God". Teilhard saw the presence of God in the heart of matter everywhere in this World, where his colleagues only saw a foreign matter which had to be forced into yielding up its secrets. He could say, like his "well-beloved friend" in *Le Christ dans la matière*: "In order to attain Him and to join Him, I have the entire Universe before me, with all its noble struggles, its impassioned seekings, and its myriads of souls to perfect and to heal. I can and I must throw myself into the midst of human activity with all my strength . . .".

Teilhard lived according to these words of his for forty years. As he wrote in *Le Cœur du Problème*: "For more than fifty years it has been my destiny to live in the closest and most intimate professional contact—be it in Europe, in Asia, or in America—with the most influential, significant, and let us say 'germinal' representatives of these countries. Well then! Thanks to these unexpected and exceptional contacts which allowed me—a Jesuit (someone, that is, brought up in the very heart of the Church)—to move about at my ease in the most active areas of thought and free research, it was only natural that certain things lying beyond the perception of those who only live in one of these two worlds should have become so clear to me that I felt myself obliged to proclaim them."

What he is proclaiming at the end of *Le Cœur du Problème* is "the possibility of believing profoundly in both God and the World, at the same time".

If we remember that it was not Teilhard's intention to define a theological position but to utter a warning cry, and that (as he himself wrote in a letter of October 12, 1926) he was not trying to agree with any of the ideas that he had heard, but only translating what he felt into words, then we will not make the mistake of reproaching Teilhard for certain errors which risked compromising the cause he was defending.

But, once this "warning cry" of his became extended into a theoretical construction built on a rational and didactic framework, we should no longer wonder that the experts in the field into which he had ventured set him questions which could only be answered in the most precise of terms, allowing for no errors or slight divergencies of meaning.

### THE ANGUISHED OPTIMIST

To the student of Teilhard one of the most striking aspects of Teilhard's character was his optimism: to Teilhard Cosmogenesis was always an ascent towards the All-high.

As a result he had been accused of evading the problem of evil, suffering and sin.

The truth is, that this optimism of his was one of the ways in which his system of thought opposed those in vogue at the time. Various existentialist philosophies, be they Christian or atheist, emphasise those aspects of man which justify a certain pessimism, such as everything irrational and absurd in the world and in man, and everything that can give rise to a feeling of abandonment, boredom, and even disgust and despair.

To say the least, Teilhard did not insist on these themes.

When he was in Paris in 1946 or in 1951 and he met Gabriel Marcel, Louis Lavelle, or Jean Hippolyte, Teilhard was always confronted by a sort of defiance inspired by modern science, or simply the feeling of the unease that nature can cause in the spirit. Yet it was not only Jean Hippolyte who could say "I was struck by the Father's optimism."

It was not only his system, but also his conversation and his letters which were free from any emphasis on evil. This may have been due to a discretion and a shyness that could be explained by an aristocratic upbringing: which taught him that it was bad manners to complain of anything. Or perhaps his taste for risk and effort, such as in his *nostalgia for the front* whose reasons he himself had so strangely analysed. His declaration in a letter of May 14, 1922 illustrates what was a kind of leitmotiv in his life: "It's no use asking if the water is cold: we must take the plunge!"

As Father Leroy wrote:* "In everything he did as in everything he taught, there was no disillusioned cynicism or bitterness, only optimism. Far from railing against men's feebleness, or the chaos in the world, he made it a principle not to believe in the existence of evil and when he could not refute the evidence of his eyes he only looked for the saving element and not for that which damns."

But there is another side to Teilhard's character, less evident

* *P. Teilhard de Chardin tel que je l'ai connu*, p. 4.

to those who never knew him, but attested to by those who had known him for long and who had lived near him: Father Teilhard was not "happy by temperament".

Let us see what Leroy has to say again: "in the matters of daily life that concerned him personally he was far from being an optimist. He patiently bore a burden which would have been too much for the stoutest heart but how often in our intimate discussions have I found him cast down, and almost discouraged! In 1939 the agonising distress he was already suffering was to intensify as the years went by, and he sometimes felt incapable of going any further: he would be prostrated by fits of weeping and he seemed to be cast down by despair."*

It was Father Leroy who accompanied him on his last visit to Sarcenat, his birthplace, in 1954: "He made no comment but his silent absorption was enough to indicate the memories that these scenes of his childhood had awakened in him.

"Frustrated by new disciplinary measures, and broken by an emotion he could hardly contain, he cut short his stay and returned to New York six weeks earlier than he had intended."†

He had suffered from emotion, anguish, sadness, discouragement, and despair, but they were far from being due to old age. He was only forty-two and a teacher at the Institut Catholique and the future seemed open and bright with promise for him when he landed in China on a mission subsidised by the Museum. On May 27, 1923, he wrote:

"I have a strong feeling that I have come to the end of my strength and that I am incapable of keeping things at a distance. When I look back on my life it seems to me that I am living in a twilight."

Might not this feeling of anguish be the key to his temperament? Yet, there was a way out from this anguish: "It seems to me that the only way out is by a blind and absolute faith in the meaning that all things, even the diminishments, must have for he who believes that all things in the universe are animated

* *P. Teilhard de Chardin tel que je l'ai connu*, pp. 43-4 and p. 28: "Later, he was to tell us of the terrible anxieties by which he had been seized and paralysed: he was to lose confidence in himself and to be troubled by scruples; despite his will-power, he was not always able to hide his anguish; the result was absent-minded or far-away expression, as sometimes noticed by more than one of his friends. . . ."

† Leroy, pp. 45-6.

by God. The further I go, the more I am convinced that the only real science—the only one we can acquire in the midst of all this weakness and ignorance—is the vision taking shape under and throughout the chaotic multiplicity of all things."*

Another phrase, which might be taken as his motto, shows where he derived his optimism: "No matter what the cost, I believe that we must cling to a belief that human agitation has a sense and a limit."†

His optimism then was always the result of his will-power fighting his temperament and the weight of obstacles frustrating him: "With the aid of his will-power, and abandoning himself to the Greatest of All, his Christ, his only purpose for living, he concealed his suffering and took up his work again, if not joyfully, at least with the hope that this personal vocation would find its fulfilment."‡

Also, how can we forget that the lives of his sisters, Françoise and Anne-Marie had brought the world of human suffering, with all its poverty and illness, to his constant attention, invading his life, as though it were not enough for him to be perpetually torn in his soul between his need to write and the fact that he had been forbidden to publish, but also had to learn what human suffering meant in the world?

A privileged witness has left us an account of this anguish:**

"(. . .) the greatest cross he had to bear was certainly that of not being understood, of seeing himself decried and almost abandoned. What sadness in his look sometimes, usually so clear and so confident! I shall never forget the last words he spoke to me at the end of our meeting in New York in February 1953 after we had spent long hours in discussing his problem alone. He was delightfully gay; at the moment of parting he put his hands on my shoulders, leant towards me and (something he had never done before) kissed me, saying: 'Pray well that I may not die embittered.' I was overwhelmed when I left him (. . .)."

Let it not be said then that Teilhard had ignored the problem of evil, even before January 2, 1953, the day on which he admitted "the increasingly important place that the explicit problem of evil was taking in his thoughts".

* Leroy, p. 27.        † Cuénot, p. 65.        ‡ Leroy, p. 44.
** F. M. Bergounioux, O.F.M., *L'âme sacerdotale du P. Teilhard de Chardin* (pro manuscripto), p. 7.

# 3

*Two Aspects of a Career*

## THE SCIENTIST

WHETHER Teilhard de Chardin was a good or a bad theologian, a good or a bad philosopher—and whether, in fact, he had ever been a theologian or a philosopher at all, in the accepted sense of the term—this has long been a subject for discussion and will probably continue to be discussed for years to come.

But one thing cannot be denied: that he was a great scientist.

In support of this assertion all we have to do is to select from among the innumerable testimonies of scientists who had known Teilhard personally and who had seen him at work. The only problem is that of selection.

For example, let us hear the evidence of Young, one of his colleagues in China:

"Although he was a Catholic, he had an exceptionally wide knowledge of the natural sciences, to my great astonishment."* Let us not minimise the astonishment felt by the young Chinaman: what astonished him so much was not only the fact that a Catholic could also be a scientist, but the "exceptional" nature of Teilhard's scientific knowledge.

In order to be a naturalist it is not enough to have a memory crammed with facts. Above all, one must be able to read Nature's great book. All who had watched Teilhard at work made similar observations to that of Georges Le Fèvre:

"His watchful eyes could pick out the smallest carved stone

* Quoted by Cuénot, p. 206.

implement, which only appeared as a red speck in the distance among the grey wind-swept wastes."*

Two of Teilhard's outstanding traits as a scientist were that he knew a great deal and that he was capable of seeing everything.

With regard to his scientific method, this is what he himself had to say concerning the rather over-adventurous methods of some of his colleagues:

"Both he and several others give me the impression that they are chasing false tracks, starting off from an insufficient basis of evidence and going beyond a certain precise area of fact into the realm of *quodlibet*. (. . .) It's a bad thing in science to have more ideas than facts."

This lapidary formula deserves to become a classic of its kind.

No matter what one may think of his adventurous approach to philosophy and theology, it should never be forgotten that Teilhard was the most prudent and least-hasty man alive when it came to science.

As it is impossible for us to go on quoting similar eye-witness testimonies to his outstanding qualities as a scientist, let us content ourselves with the quotation of the official citation made when he was made an officer of the Légion d'honneur:

"For eminent services rendered to French intellectual and scientific life, by a number of works mostly written and published in China, which have earned him an authoritative reputation in international scientific circles in general, and the Anglo-Saxon scientific world in particular. In the realm of palaeontology and geology he may now be considered one of the glories of French science, whose prestige abroad he has done so much to maintain through his personal relations with foreign scientists."

As may be expected in citations of this nature, much is made of national prestige, but, quite correctly, mention is also made of Teilhard's world-wide connections with the scientific world in which he played so great a part. Teilhard's facility for making scientific friends all over the world was a characteristic trait of his and is worth emphasising.

\* \* \*

* Cuénot, p. 117. Idem., p. 191. *Barbour's evidence*: "His piercing vision allowed him to pick out a palaeolithic object in the middle of a gravel bed three yards away, without him having to dismount."

It is impossible to reply in a word to the question, "What did Teilhard discover? What, precisely, is his claim to fame?" The truth is there was no one thing that Teilhard suddenly discovered on a certain day, all by himself. He was a modest man, as was only befitting to someone who was both a Christian and a cleric, and his modesty was all the more pleasing to his Jesuit colleagues as they recognised in him an eventual competitor.

But, more important than any modesty, was Teilhard's refusal to regard scientific work as anything but *team-work*.

We cannot separate Teilhard's scientific discoveries from all the other research work being undertaken by other scientists, who were not only his contemporaries but often his personal friends. He had both an instinctive need to make friends and a gift for finding them. This fundamental trait in his character went hand in hand with his "gift for communication". He was always putting his ideal of "Co-Reflection" into practice, in accordance with his theory of the *Noosphere*, that sphere of the mind in which all human minds should combine in their thoughts and become as one. Teilhard became more and more convinced that the time had come when to think in isolation was no longer possible, and was even without any meaning, especially with regard to an Object of such an obviously terrestrial nature as Geology or Anthropology. Towards the end of his life he became aware of the ideal he had always cherished sub-consciously, of a Science uniting both thought and life, and he spoke of a synthetic method of teaching Geology and founded an Institute of Geo-biology. From his first beginnings as a scientist, he had already regarded scientific research as being far more than a mere matter of spadework or collecting pebbles and bones: to him, it was the whole of Mankind's collective reflection on its past—"Man looking back on his Past". With such an attitude, it hardly mattered whether the discoverer of the Sinanthropus was called Teilhard, Black, Barbour or von Koenigswald—it was the discovery that mattered—not the discoverer

This is why it is somewhat difficult and even risky to say that any one discovery or theory was due to Teilhard alone, for in palaeontology, prehistoric archaeology and geology, no discovery was made and no theory elaborated without Teilhard's knowledge, without his having sometimes predicted it, and without his having often discussed it with his friends—the scientists themselves. Accordingly, to say that Teilhard "invented" anything is probably meaningless. It is equally impossible to find any discovery in his field to which he had not contributed, for he contributed to everything. It is not belittling Teilhard's scientific worth to say that he worked in liaison with all the scientists of his time: on the contrary, it is one of his greatest claims to fame.

This idea of team-work was to be one of the purest and most constant sources of joy in his life: "What luck in life, to be able to co-operate in the *birth* of something!" (December 28, 1933).

Nothing could be more mistaken than to say that Teilhard had no claim to merit because he was simply obeying the laws of modern research, which are impossible to evade, because it was part of Teilhard's merit that he realised the existence of this "law" (for such it undoubtedly is) very soon in his career, and always respected it. Such, indeed, is the opinion of others who knew him:

"Let us not forget, as is too often apt to happen, that the credit for everything we know about China, India (at least the sub-Himalayan region), Burma and Java must first go to a Frenchman, Teilhard de Chardin, even though he voluntarily remained in the background (a mistake from the national viewpoint) and never exploited the decisive role he had played in the field."[*]

"It is only just to maintain that no part of the Ancient World (where researches into Man's origins have been and are being carried out) owes as much to the individual directives and organising powers of a single scientist as China—as has been confirmed."[†]

There is no contradiction in the second quotation to what we have said before. "A single scientist", declared Movius, and he was right, for although Teilhard had always worked as a member of a team, he ended by becoming its guiding spirit and its leader without ever stepping into the limelight.

[*] R. Vaufrey, *Bulletin de la Société préhistorique française*, 1952, p. 252, quoted by Cuénot, p. 232.

[†] H. L. Movius, note dated May 21, 1952, quoted by Cuénot, p. 303, note 1.

It all began at Tien-Tsin. Although Teilhard did not find it easy to collaborate with Father Licent, it was the latter who had prepared the ground for him, as for example, when he had made the first discovery of a palaeolithic habitation in China. As a result, it was all the more easy for Teilhard's flair to detect traces of palaeolithic man in July-August 1933, for it was Licent who had led him to the right spot.

When Teilhard strayed away somewhat from Licent in order to work more closely with Peking, he noticed that the various research teams at work had divided up China between them, the Swedes taking the Sinkiang area and Tibet, the Americans the Gobi desert. Happily, there was always Black. Teilhard has left us an appreciation of Black, in which he showed that he was perfectly aware of the delicate problem of liaisons between the different scientists at work in China, and in which, unknowingly, he sketched the main lines of his own method:

"Davidson Black's extraordinary animating gifts are due, not only to his charm and the vitality of his completely human nature, but also to the universality and at the same time the perfect co-ordination of his aptitudes and views. Equally methodical in administration and bibliography, marvellously skilful in the excavation of fossils and the preparing of plaster-casts, both impulsive and ordered in research work, his professional knowledge of anatomy was combined with a very wide knowledge of Geology, Physics and Chemistry. In his eyes, the discovery of human origins was really inseparable from the problems of the general history of life and the continents (. . .) Black cherished grandiose projects that his active and determined mind almost carried to completion. (. . .) he was seriously contemplating a methodical prospecting of the mountain chains buttressing the Asiatic plateau. In India, in Baluchistan, in Persia, he was assured in a recent journey of definite eventual aid. A combined effort and a collaboration had been planned and even begun in Africa (. . .) Today no one seems able to hold as many threads together in his hands as this supremely lucid and active man had succeeded in doing."*

The reason we have quoted at such length is because this comes very close to describing the way in which Teilhard himself carried out Black's programme.

* L'Anthropologie, 1934, quoted by Cuénot, p. 100.

Teilhard's task was certainly made easier when he met such sympathetic and confiding colleagues as Barbour, who had declared, "I shared with him all the discoveries I made until I came to consider them just as much his as mine—that in the Nihowan area for example—and this went with an affection and a personal degree of intimacy which never seemed to require any explanations or excuses."*

But even when sympathy was not combined with such a profound degree of intimacy, collaboration remained the rule for Teilhard. Such was the case with Weidenreich, a German Jew, who was more authoritative and professorial by nature, and of whom Teilhard said, "Humanly speaking, Doctor Weidenreich did not have the same charm and the same animating gifts as Davidson Black." Only Teilhard simply forgot to mention himself when he wrote: "Close relations were established between the two centres at Peking and Bandoeng (Java). This was how a close collaboration began between Weidenreich and Von Koenigswald, thanks to which two so inseparably linked researches as those on the Pithecanthropus and the Sinanthropus were able to be made on two different fronts."†

Cuénot has described Teilhard's decisive influence on the organisation and synchronisation of scientific work in China, India, and Malaya.‡ The "symposium" on "Early Man", which was held at Philadelphia in March 1937, seems to have been planned long beforehand and already prepared by Teilhard in 1936, as is shown by a letter of his dated August 26th of that year. The symposium was followed by the realisation of several projects that were dear to Teilhard.

In 1936, before the symposium, Teilhard had already gone to Java. The discovery of a complete *Pithecanthropus* skull at Sangiran and the careful stratigraphic analysis of the layer in which it was found proved that the *Pithecanthropus* was a Hominien, and that the Javan Palaeolithic was linked with both that of India and China. Teilhard felt that he owed it to

* Quoted by Cuénot, p. 191. A similar friendship existed between Teilhard and Helmut de Terra. Teilhard had said, "we were like brothers" and de Terra had declared, "Father Teilhard was my friend, the most cherished and revered human being I have ever met." (Cuénot, p. 195.)

† *L'Anthropologie*, 1949, pp. 329-30, Cuénot, p. 194.

‡ Cuénot, pp. 200-1.

himself to be on the spot wherever a new find could throw some light on the problem of the *Sinanthropus*.

Teilhard's influence and presence were not always noticeable, for he did everything he could to conceal them as much as possible. Once again the modesty of the cleric shines through his work. The same virtue appears when Teilhard was discreetly revising several of his colleagues' written works: "I have a lot to do here—not only because of the results of the last trip (he had just returned from the Yellow Expedition)—but because of that famous Chou-Kou-Tien business: a memoire on the fauna or on implements to be written, or else (if they are written by my collaborators) to be completely revised" (April 6, 1932). A similar note was made on November 5, 1933. According to Father Charvet: "He corrected or rewrote scientific memoirs (of the young Chinese he had taken with him on his explorations). His name was not even on the title page. When I showed my surprise he answered, "It's all the same to me."* Cuénot gives another example of his *delicatesse*:† Teilhard wrote a memoir of some twenty-eight pages, neglected to have it published, and contented himself by signing three pages written in collaboration with his friends De Terra and Movius.

It finally became evident that no researcher in the world was better qualified than Teilhard for the task of directing prehistoric excavations on an intercontinental scale. When the question arose for the Wenner-Gren Foundation of organising excavations in South Africa on a large scale in 1952-3, the role of director was naturally assigned to Teilhard.‡

Teilhard was not only competent, he had the right touch and the right manner. In a letter dated August 5, 1953, he declared that he had been "powerfully assisted by psychology". He added, "And you know how much need my candour has of being guided from this quarter."§ Diplomacy and psychology were very necessary to Teilhard when he came as a stranger among scientists at work, who might have been set at odds among themselves by political dissensions if not by intel-

---

* Cuénot, p. 207, note 1.     † Cuénot, pp. 245-6, note 1.
    ‡ On June 27, 1953, Teilhard wrote, "There really is something for me to do there (in the way of modest supervision and animation of work)". On July 30, he wrote, "I think I can do something useful in this field in the way of organisation and *animation*."
    § Cuénot, p. 407.

lectual rivalries. The truth is that Teilhard was always successful in his dealings with them. No matter what he himself may
have said, the fact remains that he was a man of very great
talents.

In 1927, Marcellin Boule wanted to secure the services of
Teilhard for his "Museum". Teilhard had good reasons for
preferring fieldwork in an area "half the size of Europe".
When Boule wrote to tell him that he was cutting off the supply
of funds, Teilhard said, "As I shall always love him almost as a
father, I answered him as far as was possible in such a way as
not to ruffle his feathers. But you must understand that in
what concerns me I shall not deviate from the course I have
chosen" (February 27, 1927). Was this his Auvergnat stubbornness? In any case Teilhard knew how to be inflexible.

Three or four years later Teilhard found himself obliged to
choose between two friendly invitations: "Dear friend," he
wrote, "I can only come to see you on Wednesday between
6.30 and 7. I have a meeting the same day at the Trocadero
which it would be impolitic to miss."* The meeting in question
was with his friend Paul Rivet, the director of the Musée de
l'Homme. Friendship apart, it was necessary for the good of
science that Teilhard should have gone.

We now know Teilhard well enough not to misunderstand
his intentions when he said, "A powerful man is always worth
knowing",† and similarly when he spoke of the Institut de
France as a "platform from which I can make myself heard" in
a letter of June 15, 1953.

Teilhard could be obstinate and subtle, but he could also be
gentle. He writes: "Due to my gentle pressure (or else to the
force of circumstances and events) the above-mentioned
Wenner-Gren Foundation . . . has decided to concentrate its
efforts in research into fossil men in central and south Africa"
(September 21, 1952). It is very likely that the decisive factor
in his dealings, which freed him from the necessity of "diplomacy" in the sense of wire-pulling, was his absolute candour
and his total lack of self-interest in his calculations.

It is now clear how we must understand the metaphor of
the web that Teilhard used in speaking of his work in 1927
(February 27), and that of Black (in 1934). He did not mean a

* Cuénot, p. 173. † Cuénot, p. 334.

net or a spider's web in the usual sense, but rather a fine mesh that enveloped and protected a multitude of precious objects which it was vital to bring together, without a single one being lost in the process. The instrument for making his synthesis was what came to be called "the Teilhard network".

*      *      *

Let us try to list the results of Teilhard's scientific work, taking the article *La carrière du P. Teilhard de Chardin* written under his supervision for the issue of *Études* of July-August 1950 as our guide.* For the early period of his career, we have the additional information provided by Teilhard in the paper *Titres et travaux de Pierre Teilhard de Chardin†* which was drawn up when he was proposed as a candidate for the Académie des Sciences. But both texts suffer from the same deficiency: neither mentions the last stage in his career, which was by no means the least productive—his work in Africa.

Teilhard's scientific career falls neatly into four main periods:

*First period:* eleven years of palaeontological research in Europe (1912-23), from the age of thirty-one to forty-two.

As Teilhard wrote in *Titres et travaux,* etc. (page 1) this period was "mainly spent (except during the war) in the Laboratory of Palaeontology in the Natural History Museum (Paris). My work was mainly in the Palaeontology of Mammals in the middle and lower Tertiary periods in Europe: first, on the basis of old material which had not yet been studied such as the Phosphorites of Quercy, the Sparnassian of Epernay, and the Palaeocene of Reims, then, later, the description of a new material (microfauna) found in the Sparnassian of Belgium (Orsmael) by Professor Louis Dollo (. . .)."

In the eyes of palaeontological specialists the above constituted Teilhard's greatest claim to fame, for these were the works which resulted in his first important publications:

In 1914, he published *The Carnivorous fauna of the Phosphorites of Quercy.*

In 1916, *On Some Primates of the Phosphorites of Quercy,* his doctoral thesis, *The Mammals of the French Lower Eocene Period*

---

* No. 295 of the Cuénot bibliography, which adds "Article by Teilhard on himself."

† No. 274 of the Cuénot bibliography.

*and Their Strata,* and *The Mammals of the Lower Eocene Period in Belgium* (dated 1927).*

With regard to these "first studies in Palaeontology made in Europe on the basis of European material", Teilhard went on to add, "I hope they may have contributed to A) either a tidying up of our total knowledge of the Sparnassian and Palaeocene fauna of France, Belgium and England (. . .), or B) a clarification of the particularly thorny question of the Eocene and Oligocene carnivorous fauna of the Phosphorites of Quercy (. . .), or C) lastly to a better understanding of the individuality and interest of certain little-known zoological groups such as that of the curious Chiroyidae (. . .)."

Above all, it is interesting to note that it was while speaking of the Tertiary mammals that Teilhard used the image and the concept of development "in scales" of living forms for the first time. This notion was to be rich in significance and to prove particularly enlightening when Teilhard applied it to the progressive development of Man on Earth.

*Second period:* The first ten years in China (1923-33) from the age of forty-two to fifty-two. It was in Asia that Teilhard became conscious of the grandeur of the Earth and all its phenomena.

But Teilhard mostly remained in the north of China during this first stay. He was based on Tien-Tsin, as a point of departure for his explorations in the Ordos, eastern Mongolia, and Manchuria (almost as far as Siberia). Only once did he make a tentative trip southwards—to Shansi-Shensi.

He discovered the history of an entire continent "in the flexuration and granitisation of ancient socles" and in "the formation of the cloak of red and yellow earth of the Tertiary period" (he had given too recent a date to these formations: "instinctively and imprudently, I had regarded them as being transitional" (November 3, 1924), meaning that they dated from the end of the Miocene period), and in "the complexes of fauna whose establishment and evolution can be followed in their entirety at one place over a period of several million years, from the Miocene to our own day. . . ."

Undoubtedly the climax of this period came with the discovery of the traces of pre-historic man. It will be remembered

* Respectively Nos. 12, 13, 45, 86 of the Cuénot bibliography.

that it was in July and August 1923 that Licent and Teilhard became the first to discover proofs of Palaeolithic Man's existence in China.

After China Teilhard made a trip to Abyssinia, thanks to an invitation from Monfreid and the itinerary of the boat from China, and found that the Obock plateau was covered with fragments of chipped stones indicating the former presence of Man in a period separated from the date of emersion of the coral strand (late Pliocene) by the subsidence and re-emersion of the plateau.

*Third period:* the last thirteen years of his stay in the Far East (1933-46), from the age of fifty-two to sixty-five. This period began with the most striking event in his career: "his participation as adviser to the *Survey* in the unexpected discovery of the famous Peking Man" or more exactly the Chou-Kou-Tien Man or *Sinanthropus*.

Teilhard's flair played a decisive part in the recognition of the *Sinanthropus* as a *Homo faber* or tool-maker. Father Leroy has described* how, after Peï had casually picked a stone out of a drawer, Teilhard studied it attentively for a moment and then exclaimed, "This is very important, here's a carved stone." Teilhard himself was told how, after a geological section had been cut on the site at Chou-Kou-Tien, he had been "very intrigued to distinguish . . . several levels which had singular analogies with levels of 'human' habitation (in the Sinanthropus area): blackened layers . . ." (May 3, 1931).

The article in *Études* which serves as a guide to Teilhard's career goes on: "But in order to correctly situate and interpret the new and sensational fossil man nothing less was needed than a completely revised stratigraphic, physiographic and palae-ontological picture of all the Quaternary in the Far East", including India, Burma, and Java.

This was why Teilhard was to move increasingly southwards in the course of this second stage of his career: he went down the valley of the Yangtse as far as Tibet, and visited Kashmir, Java and Burma. As Claude Cuénot has said, it was a matter of establishing the geological and chronological equivalence of the strata where the Sinanthropus had been found in northern China with the strata in which the Java Pithecanthropus had

* *In Jesuites de l'Assistance de France*, summarised by Cuénot, p. 129.

been unearthed.* For this it was necessary to show that the same Quaternary and late Tertiary layers continued throughout southern China into India. Finally, "Father Teilhard . . . has the pleasure of being able to say that he has made a bridge between China and the rest of Asia, that is to say between the Quaternary layers of the different regions."†

"These far-reaching researches (in close collaboration with a team of Chinese, American, English and Dutch friends) led him to divine the individuality (both morphological and geographical) of a 'pithecanthropian' branch on the fringes of humanity in the Pleistocene of the Orient."

At the time of his entry into the Institut in 1950—the reason for this "article on himself" that we have been quoting throughout—Teilhard de Chardin was nearly seventy years old and did not yet know that the fourth and last period of his scientific career was to permit him to discover two new and unfamiliar continents: Africa and America.

*Fourth period:* the last four years of his life (1951-5), from the age of seventy to seventy-four. Since 1948 he had practically stopped making any technical contributions to geology and was only interested in Man, or, to put it more precisely, he had reached the stage where he was only interested in geology in so far as it concerned Man. This new attitude to geology was manifest in the very notion of a "Geo-biological" institute (his last achievement in Peking during World War II), and in the *new manner of teaching geology* which was the theme of his lecture at the Collège de France. This question of the relationship between geology and mankind is found again in one of the problems which occupied Teilhard's mind throughout the short final period: the problem of the *formation of the continents*, the *sine qua non* of the liberation of thought and human co-reflection.

In October 1951, speaking before the South African Archaeological Society, Teilhard declared:

"In the beginning Man was taught that his origins lay in the European Neanderthal family, and later that he was descended from the line of the Sinanthropus in Central Asia. After 1933,

---

* Cuénot, p. 228.

† Lecture given by Teilhard to the Marcel Légaut group, published in *Le Moncelet*, no. 6, p. 4, and quoted by Cuénot, p. 253, note 1.

he was led to believe that the Far-Eastern fossil-men (Pithe-
canthropi and similar forms of life) were nothing else than a
kind of side branch of Hominiens, who had probably developed
in south-east Asia, on the periphery of the main centre of
hominisation. For this reason he was very satisfied, while
visiting this country, to see how, in the light of all evidence,
man was definitely more ancient and more deeply rooted in
Africa that in Asia, both from the palaeontological point of
view at first (presence of many tertiary monkeys and development in the lower Pleistocene of the Australopithecinae), and
also culturally. For whereas in Asia stone-working activity is
scattered irregularly and discontinuously from south to north,
as if the whole Pleistocene had been necessary for Man—(first
coming from the south, then from the west, and finally from the
north) to establish himself definitely on the continent—in
South and East Africa, on the contrary, an astonishing richness
of stone implements, rising in tiers on the basis of a very old
pebble industry continuing in an Acheulian industry of an un-
believable perfection, is evident. In Europe and Asia, fossil
Man has the appearance of being a newcomer, but in this
country he shows himself to have been autochthonous."*

Such were the first fruits of this third period: Man's original
birthplace was to be sought in Africa, perhaps somewhere in
Kenya. A second gain was to be a new hypothesis on the origin
of the continents. The comparison between the African and
American continents was to result in Teilhard's orientation in
the following direction:

Written in the draft for the same lecture to the South African
Archaeological Society in October 1951 was:

*The origin of the continents.* "When I passed my examination
in geology (Haug, Termier) the classic theory was: 'The sub-
mergence of continents' (The Atlantic, even the Pacific! . . .)
"Then came Wegener: 'The drift' . . .
"Both theories postulating a partially consolidated or well
dehiscent original Quantum.
"now, as a result of my personal observations, a *third idea*
(*factor!*), the 'growth' of continents based on two phenomena:

* Cuénot, p. 391.

"*a*) The *gradual elevation* of the continental platform (more or less oscillatory but in a positive sense) = continentalisation. *b*) *Even more gradual expansion* through the marginal addition of granitised flexures . . .".*

In reality this hypothesis is inseparable from Teilhard's most fundamental convictions regarding the irreversible movement of the whole Universe towards an ever-growing Centro-complexity: it was the gradual emersion of continents that enabled the transition to be made from consciousness to reflection. This is the meaning of a note he wrote in 1953:

"Impression: Sea = immense melting-pot (Immense holo-caust) (. . .) = enormous biological mass with feeble *average-consciousness* (rate of consciousness). 'CONTINENTALISATION AND DEVELOPMENT OF CONSCIOUSNESS'. (Man: function of continents, of granitisation. . . .)"†

"And it was in this way, by a gradual process, 'from the junction made in the light of the facts, between the two related notions of the generic structure of fauna and the generic structure of continents that a third notion of the generic structure of humanity (considered as a biological unit *sui generis*, on a planetary scale) finally imposed itself in the geologist's mind'."‡

We must not take what Teilhard says about the order of sequence of these notions too literally: the idea of the generic structure of humanity did not wait for the two other "generic structures" to be noticed by Teilhard, before being formed in his mind. Teilhard's letters would seem to show that as far back as 1924 the idea of Man as an evolving planetary entity partly linked with the evolution of the planet itself had already come to him.

But this necessary reminder brings us to another aspect of Teilhard's work.

### THE RELIGIOUS THINKER

One of the many striking paradoxes in Teilhard's personality was the way in which he could reconcile an authentic scientific

* Cuénot, p. 414.     † Cuénot, p. 422.
‡ Quotation from *Titres et travaux présentés à l'Académie des Sciences*; repro-duced in the article: *La carrière du P. Teilhard de Chardin*, *Études*, July-August 1950.

attitude of objectivity, when he took part in and co-ordinated research in geology and palaeontology, with a religious philosophy which has been as much discussed as read, since publication of his religious ideas was constantly forbidden by his superiors despite the beseechings of Teilhard's many admirers.

What makes the paradox even more astonishing is that his superiors encouraged him to devote himself exclusively to profane science, while by instinct his inclination was to devote himself to a religious interpretation of the world he was studying as a scientist.

The story is a long one, and it is both that of a soul and a doctrine. Let us see if we can tell it.

This dual aspect of Teilhard's career goes back to the days of his training. But let us start when Teilhard was already fully trained, conscious of his resources and his mission, and beginning to judge the work that was henceforth to be his speciality:

"I do not have to repeat to you how little part is played by geology in the genesis of this gospel in me. I needed a contact with the Real in order to wake up and nourish myself,—and also a contact with the Real in order to take part in the 'human effort' and to practise the alliance that I had been preaching between Man and Christian. Geology has been this for me. But I believe that any other experience would have led to the same results for me" (May 26, 1925).

This is not an isolated text: "Intellectually, I am always very interested and absorbed in technical research in geology, in a domain, and in a country where there is still much to discover. Nevertheless, especially during the last two years, I have had the impression that I have become more attracted towards the study of Humanity in the present than in the prehistoric past. I conceive more and more clearly of man as the great terrestrial phenomenon, the point of culmination of great geological events, and the vastest movement of life. In other words, I am discovering the human prolongations of geology" (December 31, 1926).

He goes on to make everything clear by confiding: "Essentially, I am following—and I shall follow it as long as I have the strength—my scientific bent. But behind it, a whole religious perspective on the World and on science has been developed in my life (. . .);—and it is this above all that I wish to broadcast, rather than gain some slight fame in the sciences" (May 23, 1932).

It would seem that these quotations would allow us to state that Teilhard's main interests did not lie in purely scientific research, but rather in the religious extension of science. His real intention was not to excel in his particular field by contributing to the making of sensational discoveries: it was rather to go beyond the usual limits of his subject in order to embrace an immense object, which had so far been ignored by all existing branches of science but which was still capable of being studied scientifically. In following this new path, Teilhard realised that from this new viewpoint one would be able to see the whole of Evolution taking on meaning.

There was never any question of giving up science for Teilhard—it was simply a matter of founding a new science.

He never gave up his project for this new science, which was not really as new as one might have thought at first. Within limits, this total, synthetic science was really only a modern version of the "Physics" of the ancient Greeks. What was to be really new in the science that Teilhard wished to found was a way of teaching old subjects.

This for instance, is his idea of Geo-biology: "(. . .) defined as the science of the 'Biosphere', Geo-biology immediately shows itself to be autonomous. In other words, it does not run the risk, as might be objected, of becoming confused with other sciences such as Palaeontology, Ecology or Bio-geography in which Life is studied as much in its relation to the Past as to the Earth. Geo-biology is not simply another branch of Biology, in juxtaposition with all the other off-shooting branches, but is rather superimposed on all the other branches as a different kind of totalising principle, bringing them together, directing and concentrating them into a single group, without any possible interference, and with a double aim that is specifically and incommunicably its own:

"1. First, the study of the organic liaisons of all kinds that can be recognised between living beings, which can be considered as forming *a single closed system in their totality*.

2. Next, the study of the physico-chemical links which connect the birth and the developments of this 'closed living layer' with planetary history."*

* *Geobiologia*, Vol. I., quoted by Cuénot, p. 283.

In his *Observations sur l'enseignement de la Préhistoire* Teilhard said: "As far as I know, nowhere have lessons been given in which the *clarification* (*mise en place*), the *structure* and the *flowering* (then the compression into itself) of the human zoological group, considered as a whole, been presented technically—on the basis of precise facts, doubtless—but also with regard to the main features of their arrangement and their development."

The programme he suggested, should the Collège de France allow him to adopt it, was as follows: "In favour of, and starting from, human palaeontology and palaeo-sociology, to sketch the first outlines of a science of anthropogenesis, which is a higher and still insufficiently individualised branch of Biology."*

The science to which Teilhard was giving an ever-increasing amount of his attention was new in that it gave him a new perspective of geology and palaeontology.†

"What is past is dead and no longer interests me" (January 18, 1936). ". . . There is only one way of discovering (as taught by historical research)—by building the future. It's very simple, but there are still so many people who regard the past as being interesting in itself and who treat it as only the future should be treated" (September 1936). This was a new trend in the prehistorian's attitude: an increasing tendency to deal with the future rather than with the past. . . .

This tendency became even more strikingly pronounced in 1948: ". . . finding myself back again in this palaeontological milieu, I felt acutely (with foreseen acuity) that, except with regard to human origins (and, oddly enough, the formation of the continents—why? doubtless because it is a 'planetary' subject), the study of the Past now gives me a kind of feeling of nausea" (March 1). "This idea of a super-evolution of Humanity *in progress now* is becoming more and more my scientific platform, (. . .) Meanwhile, I have now definitely come to the conclusion here that to work on fossils (at least apart from field-work which I can no longer consider) is henceforth without any interest for me. I have decidedly made an about-face and am going forward in another direction" (April 20, 1948).

* Written on September 23, 1948, quoted by Cuénot, p. 333.
† Cf. Teilhard's letter of April 23, 1929: "One must be able to look at Humanity through the eyes of a geologist and palaeontologist."

It must not be thought that Teilhard was simply feeling "saturated" with his work for this was not one of those temporary crises well known to research workers. Once again what had happened was that Teilhard had discovered a new Object which was to polarise all his attention and his interest:

"This new contact with America will have been especially useful in helping me to find my soul a bit more profoundly: increasing lack of interest in the Past—and almost 'dazzling' realisation of the two poles of my thought and actions: 1) Man is still in an active state of zoological development; and 2) in consequence, Christian faith in God must develop a constituent in the line of human progress (which, incidentally, is the sufficient and necessary condition allowing this Christian faith, brought to the right 'pitch'—syntonised—to make the world vibrate and resound again)" (May 17, 1948).

"Knowledge of the Past is useless if it does not result in putting us on the track of movements (or processes) which are even now prolonging themselves in and around us, and which we must simultaneously espouse and control" (September 7, 1951).

\*    \*    \*

How did Teilhard reach this point in his thought?

If we try to reconstruct the inner evolution of Teilhard's religious thought, we will come across a certain number of his writings in which he has marked out his successive "discoveries". His biographer, Claude Cuénot, attaches particular importance to a letter dated June 27, 1937 (from which he has borrowed the title-headings for chapters II, III, IV, and V of his biography):

"Never before, perhaps, have I so clearly seen the possible significance of the evolution of my inner life: the purple flush of Universal Matter first transforming itself for me into the gold of the Spirit, then into the white incandescence of Personality, and finally (in its present phase) into the immaterial (or rather supra-material) glow of Love."

This text of Teilhard's takes us only as far as the half-way point in the progress of his thought. Other questions may reveal the second stage to us.

*The purple flush of matter*: the pre-scientific phase. Teilhard was still only the child who worshipped Iron, Quartz, and Fire. He had difficulty in realising that Spirit is more solid and more durable than matter. Nevertheless what he really worshipped in matter was something that went beyond palpable matter itself. . . .

*Universal matter:* Teilhard went beyond metal to discover minerals—the substance of the entire Earth—stones. As Brémond only realised later in life, we now know that Teilhard never stopped at the stage of worshipping stones alone. The adolescent thinker, who considered the flesh of Christ to be too fragile, discovered in his mind how the Incarnation of God can be, and is in fact, stronger, more solid, and more durable than anything else in the Universe. The presence and influence of the heart of the Resurrected Saviour has spread throughout the entire material universe. Such was the theme of Teilhard's *Le Christ dans la Matière* (Christ in matter). But this theme was only inspired by Teilhard's emotions (his innate love of matter) and his imagination (the image of the Sacred Heart or the fictitious description of a Christ with blurred outlines melting into His surroundings). This was Teilhard's first intuition: the Mystery of the World opens on to a Centre.

*The gold of Spirit:* Geology was to provide a rational support for Teilhard's childish intuition. Geology as the study of stones —stones in movement throughout the millions of years of prehistoric earth. These stones were for Teilhard the repositories of the Spirit. "I don't know why, but geologists have considered every concentric layer forming the Earth except one: the layer of human thought;—and those who are interested in Man are generally strangers to geology. We must unite the two points of view" (December 31, 1926). On the following January 16, Teilhard wrote: "I am planning a work on Man—not exactly prehistoric Man, but Man considered as the greatest telluric and biological event ever to have taken place on our planet. I am becoming more and more convinced that we are as ignorant of the human terrestrial layer as our ancestors were of the mountains and the oceans. . . . In other words, Geology has human prolongations which we must begin to distinguish."

Teilhard began to sketch out the theory which was soon to be expressed in the first drafts of *The Phenomenon of Man* (1928, no. 97 in Cuénot's bibliography, and 1930, article entitled

"Phenomenon of Man" in the *Révue des Questions scientifiques*, November issue): considered as an ordinary phenomenon, the apparition of thought can be compared to a kind of tidal wave which submerged the entire planet in a relatively short time so that, for a distant observer, the Earth could be seen to be covered with not only the blue and green of its oceans and plant-life, but also with a luminous layer of thought. The layer of the Spirit enveloping the Earth was to have an even greater transforming influence than bacteria. As Le Roy was to admit, the living layer of the Earth which the geologist Suess had called the *biosphere* must be regarded as being overlain by a thinking layer—the Noosphere.

How can this idea be explained? First, the apparition of the Noosphere may be explained, in retrospect, as the result of two physical laws: the *law of corpusculisation* according to which different elements form into groups, not to merge into homogeneity but to differentiate themselves into individual organisms increasingly clearly defined: and, the law of *Complexity-Consciousness* which means that as elements become more markedly individualised, they assert their inner life, first by becoming centres of action and reaction, then by becoming capable of perceiving themselves, and finally by reaching the stage of reflection.

In other words Teilhard evolved two propositions in his thought: one being that *union makes for differentiation*, the other that *complexification engenders Consciousness*.

The apparition of the Noosphere can also be explained in terms of the future, once it is realised that the great process of which it is a part leads in a certain direction: "To those who observe only the thin layer of the present, the *Animated World* seems to be slumbering, or, at least, if it propagates itself, it is only to become increasingly diversified, following some inoffensive pattern. But, seen in sufficient depth, this enormous process is moving in a *certain direction*. A wave of consciousness is streaming past the prows of the Universe. In the field open to our researches, this wave is that of Humanity."*

*The white incandescence of Personality*: In reality a Universe in which Evolution is governed by these two laws of diversification and complexification, and which moves towards the

* *La vision du Passé*, Paris, 1957, p. 263.

formation of a spiritual layer, opening on to a centre which gives it meaning: everything converges upon the Spirit. But where is this Spirit leading? Is it also moving towards a point of convergence? And if so, what is its Centre?

The answer to these questions will not be found in the pages of the *Milieu Divin* written in 1927. This made Teilhard confess: "Today, when I re-read the frankly fervent pages of the *Milieu Divin*, I am amazed to discover the extent to which the essential features of my Christo-Cosmic vision were already determined. But, on the other hand, I am surprised to see how vague and fluctuating my conception of the Universe was at this time (. . .)."*

The structure of the Universe was to become clearer and the convergence of the Spirit upon a supreme Centre was to become comprehensible, once Teilhard had rediscovered an ancient truth from his own point of view and with the help of his own knowledge: "The personal is the highest state in which we are permitted to seize the stuff of the Universe."†

In 1929 he had already observed: "After the idea of the Spiritual, that of the 'Personal' is taking on an extraordinarily increasing importance in my view of the World" (July 15).

But it was not until 1934 that he tells us: "I am studying the successive developments of an adherence which, through faith joined to faith, joins with the Christian current (or 'Phylum') by convergence. Faith in the World, Faith in the Spirit in the World, Faith in the Immortality of the Spirit in the World, Faith in the growing personality of the World" (September 23).

By degrees it could be seen that the convergence of the world of matter and life was continuing in the convergence of the world of the spirit, once it was realised that the World of Spirit was a World of Personalities. The question would then be whether the whole World did not have in its Centre a Personality who would be both Centre of the World and Centre of Convergence of Personalities at one and the same time.

". . . my present great discovery (?!) has been to perceive: 1) that the whole human problem amounts to the question of the love of God, but also 2) that the legitimacy, the psychological possibility (everywhere questioned, to my great surprise), and the triumph of this love *depend* on the *compatibility*

---

* *Le Cœur de la Matière*, 1950.    † *Études*, October 20, 1937, p. 152.

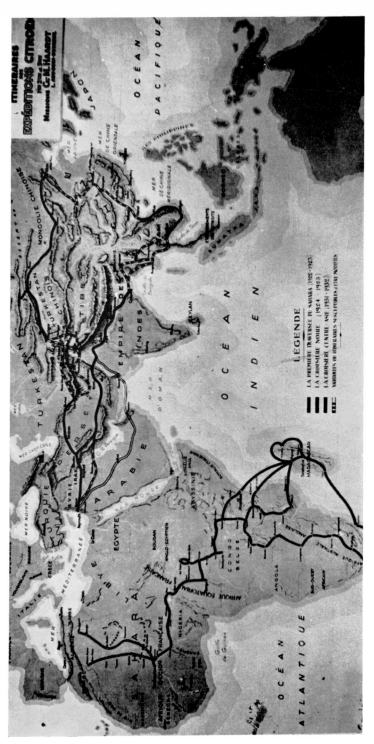

Itineraries of the Citroën Expeditions in Asia.

One of the Citroën trucks during the Yellow Expedition.

(or better—on the *essential association*) of the two terms: Universal and personal (. . .): on the whole, our World denies the Personal and God, because it believes in the Whole! What it all amounts to is that the World must be shown that, on the contrary, since it believes in the Whole it must believe in the Personal" (August 15, 1936).

Teilhard's use of a question mark followed by an exclamation mark obviously means that he uses the word "discovery" in a very special sense: what Teilhard has discovered was a very ancient truth, which was the essential truth of Christianity. If the word "discovery" can be used it is because Teilhard had discovered everything from a viewpoint which no one else had thought of adopting, in order to find whether the World and Mankind have a meaning. He took as his point of departure a positive and scientific view of evolution in order to come back to the revealed vision of the Gospel:

"In my opinion, the proper function of Christianity in the World (. . .) amounts to this: to animate (super-animate) the human effort: 1) by finding an unlimited purpose for it, going beyond the constricting circle of present cosmic dimensions, and 2) by showing it that this outlet is in a superior personal Centre which is not only theoretical, but even now partially perceptible in the domain of facts ('Revelation', Incarnation). From this double point of view Christianity appears to me as the supreme motive force behind human progress, and as the crowning of the process of Hominisation" (December 15, 1936).

*Ardour of love:* What was only regarded as a "philosophy" in 1935 was to be considered as the "mystic prolongation" of science in 1940:

"It seems to me that a 'philosophy of Union' based on an analysis of the personal structure of the Universe is both what is most needed by our modern thought, and the task in which I am most willing to collaborate" (June 16, 1935). Let it be well understood that what Teilhard was calling a "philosophy of Union" is not really a philosophy: if philosophy is a rational and theoretical process, the new subject that Teilhard had in mind consisted of a replacement of the rational by the intuitive, and was a way of life rather than speculation:

"I would wish to feel myself already free to forget for a while the scientific aspects of nature, in order to come back more

D

directly to the study of its mystical prolongations. . . ." What Teilhard is proposing, in fact, is to go beyond the stage of "knowing" to that of "action":

"What everyone must try to do in his existence is to accord the maximum reality and 'personality' to the superior Centre—as a preliminary to the specific and laborious task of contemplation" (December 7-8, 1939).

In order to explain his thought more clearly Teilhard was soon obliged to abandon the language of what is generally called "philosophy": "In the final resort, God is only attainable beyond the possession of the world, not by a negation but by a kind of *reversal* of visible things" (December 7-8, 1939).

To attain God through contemplation by "reversing" visible reality, in order to join Him as though he were a Person—this was not only Philosophy. Above all, this was a love of God above all else, and a love of all things in God.

At this point, the terms used in the *Milieu Divin* begin to lack precision: "It would be impossible for me to write something like the *Milieu Divin* again. But I seem to notice that in this first expression of what I felt, I did not explain a fundamental point sufficiently: namely, that at the end of our (holy and necessary) effort of convergence in and with all things, God can only finally be attained by means of a gesture of reversal. That veritable *positive* 'annihilation' born out of the very paroxysm of our development" (February 15, 1940).

Henceforth committed to this mystical path leading towards God, beginning with his (already mystical) acquiescence in the universal process of unification, Teilhard was now able to come back to all the scientific and practical activities of Mankind to give them a new coefficient, and to add a new element to them. He did not upset established geology and theology by adding any foreign or disruptive element to these two studies: all he asked was that, as a new dimension of total reality had been discovered (genesis, drift, evolution . . .), traditional geology and theology should assume additional significance by *taking account of this newly discovered fact.*

In short, it was finally necessary to seriously consider the "sense" that every object and activity has in relation (or by virtue even of its organic relation) with the totality of Reality-in-movement in any branch of study or Science.

In other words, in any study of human activity it was henceforth to be necessary to take serious account of the connections between the subjects of these activities and the totality of Reality-in-movement. Take, for example, Anthropology:

"So far, Anthropology has been generally considered as a pure and simple description of Man, past and present, individually or in Society. Henceforth its main purpose should be to guide, promote and operate Man's evolution forward. Non-biologists often forget that, underlying the varied laws of Ethics, Economics and Politics, certain general and imprescriptible conditions of organic growth have been incorporated into the structure of our universe. To determine these basic conditions for biological progress in the case of Mankind should be the special aim of the new Anthropology—the science of Anthropogenesis, the science of the ulterior development of man."*

Let us take another example, this time with regard to theology:

"Recently, I have regarded the entire *nucleus* of my inner perspective as being something wholly dependent on and 'deductible' from the mere transposition of the vision traditionally expressed in terms of the *Cosmos* into the *dimensions of Cosmogenesis*: Creation, Spirit, Evil, God (and, more specifically, Original Sin, Cross, Resurrection, Parousia, Charity . . .),—all these notions, carried over into the dimensions of 'genesis' become amazingly clear and coherent" (January 1, 1951).

The practical consequences of this attitude can be deduced logically: Anthropogenesis was to become a science of the control of man's ulterior evolution. With or without the help of Julian Huxley, Teilhard hoped to set up an international body for this purpose (Huxley-Teilhard correspondence, 1951). But, in Teilhard's eyes, the real hopes of Anthropogenesis did not lie in any human institution, for a better one existed already—the Church.

". . . forced, as we are, out of the static Aristotelian cosmos, and brought (by the entire system of modern Physico-chemical-biology) into a universe in a state of Cosmogenesis, we must henceforth re-think all our Christology in terms of Christogenesis (similarly all our Anthropology in terms of Anthropogenesis). Such an operation is not just a matter of local

* Quoted by Cuénot, pp. 342-3.

adjustments. As a result of the addition of a new dimension, everything must be re-founded (as in geometry, when one makes the transition from the circle to the sphere).—A magnificent endeavour out of which, I can guarantee you, Christ emerges truly triumphant and as the saviour of Anthropogenesis" (April 28, 1954).

Two conditions were implied: on one hand, all the traditional truths of Christianity had to be maintained intact; and, on the other hand, these truths were to be re-clarified and re-illumined gradually by the new light that was henceforth to shine from a World that was better studied and better understood.

The traditional truths of Christianity were to be maintained intact. Let us single out one of them that our modern world has difficulty in recognising as a certainty: that of immortality. Teilhard very frequently stressed the despair, and as a result the discouragement, the refusal to make an effort, and finally the end of self-evolution that would result if each of us and the whole of humanity were to believe in a truly "total" death.

The idea of a new clarification of these truths in the light of the notion of Universal genesis may be resumed by means of a diagram, such as that provided by Teilhard in *Le Cœur du Problème*:* starting from a centre O, the vector OY indicates the On-High, the vector OX the Onward.

"Here (following OY) we have Faith in God, indifferent, if not hostile, to any idea of an Ultra-evolution of the human species. There (following OX) we have faith in the World, which is formally a negation (at least in words) of the idea of all transcendant God.

"OY and OX, the On-High and the Onward: two religious forces (. . .) henceforth confronting each other in the heart of every man; two forces (. . .) which become feeble and perish if they are isolated;—two forces as a consequence (. . .) which await one thing only: not that we should have to choose between them, but that we should find some means of combining the two."†

To achieve this conjunction, we must draw the line OR: "Christian faith, 'rectified'‡ ('made explicit'), and the problem is solved: and the way that is both On-High and Onwards, it

---

* *L'Avenir de l'Homme*, p. 349.      † *L'Avenir de l'Homme*, pp. 344, 345.
‡ The choice of the word is unfortunate and confusing.

lies in a Christ who is both Saviour and motive force not only for the individual human being but for the whole of Anthropo-genesis."*

This text, which was aimed at those who "are charged with the direct or indirect guidance of the Church" dates from 1949.

In his remaining years of life, Teilhard was to affirm his belief with increasing vigour:

"I always feel that the Church is phyletically essential to the completion of the human" (August 16, 1951).

"Naturally, Christianity (and that alone) shows itself capable of stimulating human energy *to the depths* AND *in its entirety*".

Three months before his death, Teilhard asked that he should be regarded as "a man who is trying to express frankly that which is in the heart of his generation: the irrepressible need to save and to mutually intensify the radiance of an Ultra-personal God, and the immense organisation of the fantastic Cosmogenesis which is now revealing itself before our eyes" (January 25, 1955).

* *L'Avenir de l'Homme*, p. 349.

# 4

## Teilhard as Thinker

WHETHER I want to defend or attack Teilhard's thought depends on whether I am discussing it with his detractors or his partisans. His detractors quote from Teilhard's own writings in support of their contentions. His partisans quote from others, and reproach their opponents with quoting out of context. As a result, anyone who wishes to be an impartial judge in the dispute will be forced to recognise that it is no use quoting Teilhard: the only solution is to read not *some* of his writings but *all* of them. In some he will find Teilhard confessing that he is a natural pantheist, and that monism is the basis of his system of thought; in others, he will find Teilhard declaring that there are different kinds of pantheism, the best being that of Saint Paul,* and in yet another he will find Teilhard saying that his monism is simply his sense of the essential unity of the world. When, for example, Teilhard categorically affirms that the spirit is engendered by the complexification of matter, his statement is immediately qualified by a foot-note saying that this statement is only valid from a phenomenological point of view.

Thus, in reply to one of Teilhard's opponents, I only have to cite the context of his remarks. When I am discussing his work with one of his partisans, I will always be able to cite other texts of Teilhard's to support my view, which my

* I Corinthians 15. 28. "God is all in all things."

interlocutor will then refute by explaining them in the light of what Teilhard really *meant* to say. . . .

Strangely enough, it would seem that whereas Teilhard's supporters always seem to know what he *did* mean to say, his detractors always seem to know what he did *not* mean to say. The remarkable consequence is that despite all the protests, accusations, and refutations that have been inspired by Teilhard's views, no one has ever (as far as I know) accused him of being a heretic. Not only "is it clear that all his intentions are pure and that his work is obviously inspired by a very powerful sense of charity and love of truth", or "it does not seem that his theses inspired by *faith* are explicitly altered in their meaning", but also "it cannot be stated that there are any obvious heresies as such in his system".* On one hand, Teilhard states unequivocally that he wishes to uphold official dogma, and on the other hand the authorities responsible for safeguarding the purity of the faith have never formally condemned any of Teilhard's theses. Even apart from all this, Teilhard's work is so suffused with apostolic charity that not one of us can feel that he has the right to question the purity of his faith.

Must we then distinguish between what Teilhard said and what Teilhard meant to say?

Another quotation may bring us nearer a solution to the problem: "Even those who were the most opposed to his philosophical and religious views recognised his exquisite gift of sympathy which made him a catcher of souls."† And indeed, in discussion with those of Teilhard's supporters who knew and loved him, who had talked with him and met him, it becomes obvious that they are still under the spell of "L'esprit Teilhard". It is understandable enough, surely, that no text, however formal, can match the certainty of the views held by those who had actually come into contact with Teilhard?

It can be said that there were two paths of access to that unformulated inner world of Teilhard's: one was the direct path of sympathetic understanding in conversation with Teilhard and even more, in living with him, the other, indirect, was by a methodical and critical examination of his writings.

---

* Anon., *L'évolution rédemptrice du P. Teilhard de Chardin*, pp. 10, 93, 148, etc.

† P. Leroy, *P. Teilhard de Chardin tel que je l'ai connu*, p. 63.

There are, therefore, two possible ways of reconstructing Teilhard's thought: by reading his works and taking into account
his intentions in writing them as far as possible, or else by
isolating his intentions and by examining, as objectively as
possible, what those readers who did not have the good fortune
to hear from Teilhard's own lips should be able to find in his
writings.

\*          \*          \*

It would seem that the anonymous author of *L'évolution
rédemptrice du P. Teilhard de Chardin* (The redeeming evolution
of Father Teilhard de Chardin) had chosen the second way.
He did not ignore Teilhard's intentions; instead, he simply
abstracted them and made a minute study of his writings. Unfortunately he only had four of Teilhard's written works at his
disposal, which gave him rather a limited basis for his study.
Moreover, noticing that Teilhard was dealing with philosophical and theological subjects as was only to be expected in
a profession of faith (*Comment je crois*, How I believe) and a
little treatise on the inner life (*Le Milieu divin*, Tien-Tsin,
November 1926-March 1927 (not 1937), the author felt
himself obliged to interpret Teilhard's propositions and terms
according to the same norms which would have been necessary
for any straightforward work on philosophy or theology,
properly speaking.

The result was that he attached a rigorous, strict meaning
to words and expressions that Teilhard could only have used in
an approximative, wide, figurative sense, such as "monism",
"pantheism", "necessity", "personal universe", "collective
consciousness", "super-humanity", "Cosmic Christ", "no
fundamental distinction between the physical and the moral",
"super-personalisation", "union with the Centre or Limit of the
evolution process", "ultra-concentration of personal human
elements in a higher personal consciousness", etc. . . .

All this new terminology sounds strange when quoted by
someone who had been trained in the traditional schools—
all the more as Teilhard had never bothered to take the pre-
caution of supplying the definitions for his terms. Consequently
the author of this work had no difficulty in showing that a
reading of these works "could result in rather dangerous

attitudes", and in warning his readers that "one must have . . . a thorough theological training not to go astray in a naturalist interpretation of dogma".* Similarly: "For those without sufficient or strong enough theological training, the Christian evolutionism that the Father proposes, risks imperilling the fundamental tenets of faith and leading many minds into grave theoretical and practical errors."†

Doubtless. But it might have been just as prudent to have warned the reader that Teilhard did not mean his works to be read as if they were those of a theologian or a philosopher. Knowing that Teilhard intended to remain absolutely faithful to traditional Catholic faith, the reader would then have asked "what he had meant to say"—even if he had to reproach Teilhard for not having always expressed himself clearly enough.

It is therefore understandable that Teilhard's reply to this little book should have been:‡ ". . . I really do not recognise the expression of my thought in it. Not even in the title where the idea is insinuated that I attribute a saving virtue to the fact of becoming Cosmic; for, on the contrary, my constant preoccupation was to make a personal and transcendant Christ radiate the 'redeeming' properties of the suffering engendered by Evolution."

*    *    *

The method used by a hostile critic of Teilhard's thought was also to be that of one of his admirers (who was, however, far from being an uncritical disciple). Doctor Viallet recognised Teilhard's sincere desire to remain a good Catholic in total submission to the Church. He also realised§ that Teilhard was trying to defend St. Thomas Aquinas's authority as well as the scientific evidence for evolution,—and that he hoped to find certain confirmation for his theories in scholastic writings, searching for parallels between certain aspects of his thought and various arguments of the Aquinist schools.

But Doctor Viallet put Teilhard's convictions and intentions

* p. 154.    † p. 9.    ‡ *Études*, September 1950, p. 284.
§ François-Albert Viallet, *L'Univers personnel de Teilhard de Chardin*, pp. 215 and 235. We know from a very authoritative source that there was strong disagreement between Teilhard and Dr. Viallet, some of whose theses seemed "frankly heretical" to Teilhard.

"between parentheses". He concentrated exclusively on those formulae of Teilhard's which he considered to be revolutionary, and accorded them philosophical status. In Teilhard's work he saw a philosophy which had nothing in common with the traditional teachings of the Church. It seemed to him that Teilhard was replacing the philosophy of being with the philosophy of union: "To be is to unite oneself, or to unite others".* God only exists in the act of uniting himself,—thus, the Trinity. Similarly divine creation is the result of multiplication and union around God.† Evil is only the inevitable by-product of this process of synthesis which is creation.‡ Taking Teilhard's formula "Supernatural can only mean Supremely Real"§ literally, as though it were part of a theological treatise, Viallet saw it as evidence of an "endeavour to recast spiritualist thought", as a way of establishing "the new God" that the modern world was awaiting.**

As we can see, Viallet was going much further than the anonymous author of *L'évolution rédemptrice*: what he admired in Teilhard's writings was much more serious than what the other had condemned. . . .

The same question arises with regard to both these conflicting interpretations: how far are we right in ignoring the intentions expressed by Teilhard?

*     *     *

What then, are the intentions expressed by Teilhard, that we can no longer afford to ignore if we are to have a chance of discovering his thought by reading his texts?

In 1947†† Mgr. Bruno de Solages was able to distinguish them clearly after reading the first pages of the *Human Phenomenon*:‡‡ "At the first reading, the reader trained according to the usual curricula of the seminaries will be easily disconcerted. He will ask himself exactly what he is dealing with: is it science? is it philosophy? is it theology? (. . .) Every error of interpretation has a common source: in reading these pages the reader is not adopting the view-point from which the author wrote

---

* *L'Univers personnel de Teilhard de Chardin* p. 236.     † p. 237.     ‡ p. 239.
§ p. 249.     ** p. 253, but cf. p. 218, note 1.
†† *Bulletin de Littérature ecclésiastique*, pub. by the Institut Catholique of Toulouse, October-December 1947, no. 4.
‡‡ 1955 edition, p. 21.

them; for, no matter what some may think, Teilhard was perfectly conscious of his purpose, his method, the field in which he was writing, and the angle from which he was tackling reality (. . .). What then is his point of view? It is not the habitual point of view of the Christian philosopher who studies man, from the inside, but rather that of the scientist. Father Teilhard de Chardin studies man from the outside, as he would appear, one might say, seen through some prodigious telescope on the planet Mars: the observer would not see inside man and would be less struck by the sight of one individual than by the sight of the whole of mankind, Teilhard's point of view is objective and global. (. . .) This view of the whole— essentially from a phenomenological point of view is therefore by definition incomplete, since Teilhard is not studying reality in depth; he is not substituting a new kind of metaphysics, nor, even more obviously, a new kind of theology (. . .). It follows that the author was not dealing in his writings with theological questions, properly speaking, which can be picked out at random. To do this would be to confuse the picture. And to demand that he should only write about cosmology on condition that he himself should also provide the solutions to all the theological problems arising out of his new perspectives is a doubly excessive demand. First of all theological problems can only be resolved by a theological method, and the task of resolving them is for professional theologians. Next, to demand that a thinker should only explain his synthesis after he has answered all the questions to which it may give rise is to ask the impossible."

It now becomes clear that Teilhard did not intend to write theology. This is especially evident in *The Phenomenon of Man* which was published in 1955, but it is less evident in the various unpublished writings which had been privately circulating since 1935, for the question is: did Teilhard's formal intention of not *writing theology* preserve him at all times from ever doing so in fact?

According to the testimonies of his best and closest friends, the contrary appears to be the case.

In his same speech of November 18, 1947, Mgr. Bruno de Solages mentioned some of Teilhard's non-published writings, which he called "partial studies . . . written for non-believers, which competent authority has judged inopportune for publication"; he also protested against "the indelicate use made of these texts in public controversies" and observed that "read with more enthusiasm than perspicacity by young insufficiently trained people who have only known them very incompletely, they have often been misunderstood", finally adding that "As I cannot help being a demanding theologian, I could not counter-sign all these writings, all bearing different dates and witnessing to the constant progress of Teilhard's thought."

Similarly, the Reverend Father Bergounioux, professor of geology and palaeontology at the Catholic Institute of Tou-louse, whose profound friendship for Teilhard cannot be doubted, made the following observations during a *Requiem* for the repose of Teilhard's soul on July 10, 1955:

"Such an interpretation of various domains of human thought was not without its grave dangers. Who can boast of having a sufficiently precise knowledge of all the various theo-logical, philosophical and scientific subjects to be able to pronounce on them with the precision justly required of the specialist? The grandeur of this man was simply to have faced this risk, with the certainty of being contradicted in terms that were not always measured. However, we must not be surprised by the severe criticisms that were sometimes levelled against him; when a Catholic theologian is faced with an intellectual synthesis of this scope, it is his duty to consider it in the im-mutable light of Revelation. Even if certain traditional posi-tions may be abandoned, dogmatic truth must always be safeguarded. And it must be admitted that this idea of Christo-genesis, the work of a Universe moving towards the Omega point, the glittering goal of Humanity, can cause confusion in the mind. It is difficult to understand how this collective taking stock of conscience can lead to an appeal for super-personalisa-tion. It may be that all these questions take one beyond the possible limits of human intelligence which attains its full grandeur as it reaches its limits."

It only seems logical to conclude that if Teilhard had kept firmly to his resolve of never intervening in theological matters throughout his entire career from the very beginning, and if he had shown this resolve in words and deeds, then neither his superiors, his detractors, nor his admirers would ever have found anything in his unpublished writings that could be called contestable, ambiguous, or even indefensible. . . .

But the contrary was to be the case from the very beginning. "What sparked off the crisis", wrote Claude Cuénot,* "were certain of the Father's ideas and a certain paper of his on the difficult problem of original sin." Father Leroy has stressed† that "Errors of theological interpretation crept into a note in which he expounded his new vision of the universe" and "I do not question the ambiguity of some of Father Teilhard's statements . . .".‡

In conclusion, it would seem that Teilhard's conscious, open and formal intention of not broaching theological subjects was only fully realised in his later works such as *The Phenomenon of Man*. Elsewhere, everything leads us to believe that instead of simply contenting himself with uttering the warning cry of "he who sees", Teilhard found himself unable to resist the generous desire to reform and to transform whatever seemed to him to be unadapted and obsolete in traditional theological concepts.

\*　　　　　\*　　　　　\*

Another question remains to be answered.

Does what we have said with regard to Teilhard's attitude to theology also apply to his philosophical writings? Mgr. Bruno de Solages assures us that Teilhard's intention was to confine himself to the domain of phenomena and that we must not look for metaphysics in his writings.

But this is far from clear, at least as far as we can judge from the disagreements on this point between Teilhard's admirers, whose admiration for him does not prevent them from voicing their doubts and moderating their expressions of approval.

In his fundamental book on Teilhard, Claude Cuénot never hesitated in providing a kind of philosophical balance sheet at the end of each stage in the life of his subject. He is obviously convinced that Teilhard had a philosophy of his own which, moreover, was a philosophy of the future and perhaps the only one capable of reconciling Christian and modern scientific thought.

\* p. 85.　　　† pp. 31-2.　　　‡ p. 53.

In his *Introduction à la pensée de Teilhard de Chardin* (Introduction to the thought of Teilhard de Chardin), Claude Tresmontant strongly defended a completely opposed point of view: in support of his contention he quotes* from writings of 1916, *La vie Cosmique* (Cosmic Life), *L'Hominisation*, 1923, *Esquisse d'un Univers personnel* (Outline of a personal universe), 1937, *La place de l'Homme dans l'Univers* (Man's place in the universe), 1942, *La Centrologie* (Centrology), 1944, *Vie et Planetes* (Life and planets), 1946, which all go to show that before he had written *The Phenomenon of Man*, Teilhard was conscious of carrying out a purely and strictly scientific task.† He adds: "This scientific and phenomenological method of research was Teilhard's own method, in which he excelled. Teilhard fully realised that he was above all a 'physicist' in the widest sense of the term: 'I am neither a philosopher, nor a theologian, but a student of the "phenomenon", a physicist in the old Greek meaning of the word.' "

The only additional piece of information that Tresmontant gives us with regard to this problem of Teilhard's first writings dates from the 1914-18 War: he tells us that they "comprise metaphysical and mystic speculations".‡ Moreover, it can be seen in certain passages in his writings and in *Comment je crois* (How I believe) that he remained faithful to a certain number of metaphysical theses which were only an appendix to the main body of his work.

Similarly Doctor Paul Chauchard§ defends Teilhard from the accusation that he ever trespassed, be it ever so slightly, on the domains of philosophy. He tries to explain the proper aim of scientific phenomenology: the spirit of synthesis, the endeavour to see each phenomenon not only in its totality which even includes the "subjective" aspect, but also in its objective relation to all other phenomena. The result is the objective manifestation, on the same level as science, of a certain objective sense of the phenomenon. This brings one very close to the philosophical domain, without ever entering it. And if it should happen that the "phenomenologist" (in the new meaning which owes everything to Teilhard and nothing to Husserl) should reveal the presence of God, the soul, or some moral

---

* pp. 19-22.    † p. 23.    ‡ p. 110.
§ *L'être humain selon Teilhard de Chardin*, passim.

imperative behind the phenomena, it is obvious that only the philosopher is equipped to bring the work to a conclusion. Dr. Chauchard is fully in agreement with Tresmontant when he writes: "Certainly the vision of a world so discovered has philosophical values and implications, but this vision of the world only affects the philosopher inasmuch as it is constituted by ways and methods which are strictly free from all extra-scientific pre-suppositions."*

## THE SOLUTION

Following the testimony of Teilhard's friends and disciples, we arrive at a credible and a somewhat modified conclusion: Teilhard *did* practise theology and (not necessarily sound) philosophy, but only in despite of his deepest intention which was to do something quite new which no one else had ever ventured to do with the possible exception of the ancient Greeks, such as Aristotle in the *Physics* and Plato in the *Timaeus* (with the difference that these two works certainly have a large content of philosophy).

By a series of gradual steps forward, Teilhard was thus led to practising a mental discipline which was as distinct from pure science as it was from philosophy and theology. He was providentially impelled in this direction by the fact of his uncomfortable and hybrid condition as a man of God living in the world of profane science whose progress he did so much to further. As with great inventors, it was only gradually that he clearly realised what he wanted to do, and what lay within and which he was to designate by the names of "Ultra-physics".

Even if we reproach Teilhard for not having clearly realised at the very beginning what he felt, without being able to define it exactly to himself, we must still recognise objectively that he was, unwittingly, a philosopher and a theologian besides being a "phenomenologist" or a "hyper-physicist". As Tresmontant said, it was because "the vision of the world so discovered had philosophical implications and values", and therefore a scientist practising the science of hyper-physics needed to be able to control his *libido sciendi* and his natural curiosity to an uncommon degree in order to know when to stop. Such

* *Introduction à la pensée de Teilhard de Chardin*, p. 23.

"intellectual moderation" is only feasible for someone who has decided to confine himself to hyper-physics alone.

I have shown elsewhere* how Teilhard was led, against his will, into philosophy despite his increasingly firm intention of only devoting himself to hyper-physics. I have also said why this philosophy of Teilhard's does not always seem to me to be of very great worth. It is now time to turn over a page, and to explain why even the most traditional philosopher should lend an ear to Teilhard's "cry" and contemplate the "vision" that impelled Teilhard to utter this cry . . .

What follows is not a *resumé*, but only a first attempt to explain in traditional terms what Teilhard wanted to make us hear. What he said with regard to one of his shorter works holds good for the whole of his thought: "If you read it, do so with indulgent understanding. I am walking with the heavy tread of an elephant on the best raked flower-beds in the garden of scholasticism. Forget the casualness and try to see what I have wanted to express. Probably it is possible to transcribe me into orthodox characters" (Letter to Reverend Father Fessard, May 16, 1936). It is true that some twenty years before, he seemed to fear that to express himself in orthodox terms would result in an impoverishment of his thought. "The philosophical part [he is writing of a short work of his entitled *La Multitude*] is obviously very approximative, and even Manichean in appearance. I have left it as it is, for lack of being able to express myself better, and because it seems to me that a 'direction of truth' lies hidden under slightly false or contradictory terms, which would be impoverished if I used language that was more correct in its logic and its surface orthodoxy" (letter to Mlle Teilhard-Chambon, March 24, 1917).

We have now taken the risk of impoverishing and banalising his thought, with the wish that others may succeed better. . . .

Nevertheless, we have tried to respect the way in which Teilhard's thought has progressed. We think that in this way we will obtain a kind of philosophical *apologia* which will permit a reconciliation between a purely profane view of the world and a Christian interpretation of its future. But we are far from being sure that this will lead us to a complete Christian philosophy: for this would imply a recognition of the Word

* *Pierre Teilhard de Chardin ou le Philosophe malgré lui*, Beauchesne, 1960.

incarnated as the First-born of every creature, and therefore, not only as He towards whom we are carried by every movement of creation, not only as He who came into this movement in order to help it to completion, but as He in whom this movement found its origin and its meaning in the very beginning. Christogenesis does not end in Christ: it begins by HIM.

## THE CRY AND THE VISION

"On-high and onward!" On-high is the Transcendance of God; onward, is the necessary immanence of our goal in life. Modern man has refused to connect with God On-high because too much lies before him to be done. Modern man refused God because God is perfect and only that which remains to be perfected interests him. The modern world must be shown that God is not only above us On-high but also in front of us— Onward—and not something yet to be "realised", but rather something that must be made "for us", brought "into us" and "among us", as is necessary for us and as he wishes. His name is holy, but it is up to us to sanctify it; his reign is universal, but it is up to us to make him reign; his will is done, but it is up to us to accomplish it. This does not mean in any way that we should leave our real, natural world behind us for the question is not that men should turn away from the things of this world, but only that they should "reverse" the things of this world, and thus cease seeing them from the wrong side so that they may finally see them from the only side in which their true value becomes apparent—the side of God.

But, we may object, is it not anti-human, anti-modern and anti-scientific to claim that the things of this world only have value if seen from the side of God?

On the contrary: the cry of "On-high and onward!" which has always been heard by truly religious men has never been more adapted to man's necessities as it is now, and has never been more firmly justified than it is at present by science at its most modern.

By science, we do not mean science as it has been practised since August Comte, in a spirit of positivism. To want to observe data, record and measure facts, classify them and observe the links between them—all this is excellent enough but it is also quite insufficient. Our spirit wants to "see", and "to see" is to

"unite", and "to unite" is to connect. The need to make one
fact connect with another leads the spirit to a still greater
ambition which is to connect all facts together. This ambition
which was beyond man's capacities a century ago is now perfectly feasible. Every law and every fact that is capable of being
reached by human science is now in the process of spontaneously
merging before our eyes into one great symphony—a marching
song for humanity or the song of a great epic saga.

A law of recurrence, reappearing at each successive stage of
reality, obliges us to recognise the permanent existence of a
universal rule in every event in natural history, human history
and evangelical history: everything that was scattered becomes
united in one, and everything that was one becomes divided
into many. Both operations of this law are equally real but only
the first is creative. To create something new, consistent and
durable in natural creation, historic invention, or the generosity
that saves is always to unite something. To unite does not mean
to unite in any way, for the union that creates, stimulates or
saves is never an act of absorption into a homogeneous mass in
which the things united lose their identity, but is always the
exaltation of the old in a new which becomes diversified.

However, the permanence of this law must not make us forget
that it applies on various levels which cannot be confused: the
theme is stated, the variations follow. The same law applies one
way in the body, another way in the mind and in yet another in
divine grace. The bodies that existed cease existing so that a new
and superior body may exist in their place. But the spirits that
existed cannot cease to exist so that a higher spirit may exist in
their place. For them, complexification consists in raising all
there is of richness and fertility in physical complexification on
to the spiritual level, by transposing it on to the level of knowledge and love. Thus, what in the mineral and vegetable world
was formerly only an opaque innerness of the body closed in on
itself, and what in the animal was presence to the other and to
itself in an elementary state of consciousness, becomes in man a
presence to all reality, a presence to oneself and to others in
the heart of the Whole. In the Christian, this finally becomes
the habitation of God in Man, the merging of Man into God,
the incorporation of Humanity into the Son of God until
Christ reaches maturity.

Modern science confirms this hierarchic and ancient view in more than one way: it provides us with a deep understanding of the process, by showing, in fact, how it takes place. Science invites us to choose the second of two images, both possible *a priori*: one, that of a universe that was completely and definitely formed in the beginning, the second that of a universe incompletely formed at first and now in the process of gradually forming itself. Ranging from geology to sociology, by way of every branch of physiology and also the physics of the cosmos, the hypothesis of evolution offers us a coherent and unifying explanation, despite its undeniable obscurities of detail. If we accept it, as most of the scientists of our time have done, then the more complex higher forms are not simply in hierarchical juxtaposition to the others, but proceed from them: a sign that the Whole of which they are a part contains its own law, and an inner force which takes everything by a natural movement towards an increasingly complete and ever more total Good.

The presence of Man in the universe and the place he has in it will then take on a "meaning" independent of any metaphysical system and any religion:

Man is not in the world by chance if his apparition continues and completes a long series of partial successes which were inferior to him and which were obscurely preparing for his appearance.

The existence of Man in the World is not absurd if it can explain and justify itself: explaining itself by its preparations, and justifying itself by the opportunity that each man has of understanding and making use of everything, and subduing everything to his own ends.

Man is not in the World for nothing, he is not superfluous in it, for he is in it for his Good and to find what he needs to better himself. The past as discovered by the theory of evolution answers for the future as predicted by the line of evolution. Obviously, everything tends to make us think that man's future will not mean a transition from the human to the superhuman, if it be true that the spirit is already the means of grasping all, the Whole, and that it can only progress in the sense of an increasingly perfect understanding of the Whole. The human body can become more and more adapted to the service of the Spirit, but that the Spirit should become more spiritual can only have meaning in the sense of intellectual and moral progress.

The destiny of individuals can therefore vary greatly. Some may completely renounce making use of the world, while others may only accomplish their own perfection through this very use of the world. This should not surprise us, if it be true that every spirit is made for the Whole of the true and the good, while every spiritual person still remains free to choose his own path leading towards this Whole. There is at least evidence that a spirit does not save itself, and does not justify itself alone; men only save their own spirit by saving themselves all together thus saving the world with them.

In this ineluctable law we can find the essential dignity of the "person" again, revived and magnified by the dignity of all nature, for the whole of nature unconsciously recognises that it is a part of a Whole which surpasses it and whose good is better than it and greater than its own good. A person may confess that this is his own destiny, but he is, moreover, capable of perceiving the Whole and freely integrating himself in it: nothing then, in a certain sense, is more natural than the movement by which a person turns towards a Good which surpasses him and which surpasses his own good, and nothing is more superior to mineral or animal nature than this conscious and voluntary acceptance of a law which only exalts what is irreducible in a person by incorporating it in a Whole. The dignity of the individual lies in this: one is never as perfectly oneself as when one is prepared to sacrifice oneself for the Good of that Whole of which one is a part.

But is the individual really part of a Whole? Is there some higher Good than one's own Good? Naturally every man feels that it is good to deny himself something for the good of the family or political group of which he is a part. The animal feels the same in his way, and even the organism shows us the hand exposing itself for the defence of the good of its all which is its body.

Nothing then is more natural for the human spirit than to feel the need to strive towards a higher good which is not merely its own. This natural law which, in man, becomes the supreme moral law, is only a transposition into spiritual terms of a law which has been constantly verified at every level in nature, and at every stage in the evolutionary process.

It remains to be asked how this most modern and most profoundly natural of mankind's aspirations is to be achieved in deeds: the aspiration to reproduce and surpass in its spirit and together with all spirits, the universally natural law which states that all parts have no greater good than that of their Whole.

Naturalist solutions are no more satisfactory than purely political or social solutions.

The Good of the Whole which is also the Whole of the Good, is neither an abstract notion, nor a common property, nor an optimum juridical state . . .: "individuals" can only be magnetised by a Good which is also an individual.

This is borne out by the whole profane and religious history of humanity: it is not below it, nor even in itself, that Humanity is seeking for the Good that will give meaning to the whole of Humanity and not just a few individuals—it is above itself that Humanity seeks the Good.

This is where Christianity comes into the picture. The Good of the Whole and the Whole of the Good, the Centre of the Universe towards which all desires, all movement, all becoming, converges, is itself immersed in this world and in this humanity. It is now the effective but invisible Head of a Body in which men are united like the various members of a single organism. It is henceforth at the end of all evolution, all history. It is He who must come and who comes to unite in His ever-growing Person all our own persons, and all who have agreed to remain free from all attachments to earthly things while still using them, in order only to attach themselves to His Person.

*        *        *

What was the little boy really looking for when he lost himself in contemplation of his God of Iron? He was looking for plenitude, for the Unique, necessary, and sufficient Element in life, in which he hoped to find Consummation, Completion and Consistency.

And when he had learned Iron is prone to rust, what was it that he sought in planetary matter, in the Stuff of things, in the Elementary that is present everywhere—whose ubiquity makes for incorruptibility? Why was he seeking for a contact and communion with the full, the hard and the durable?

And what did he finally find when geology and the theory of evolution had shown him a higher form of the Constant and the Durable, i.e. the Convergent?

What he discovered he called Matter, whose glorious underlying unity he had found behind its appearance of diversity and multiplicity, and in which a Being was everywhere present—a Being which could attract one like a spirit, which was as palpable as a solid body, as vast as the sky, a Being which suffused all things and which was yet different from all things. Teilhard thought he saw God as Consistency, as the Full, the Durable, and especially as God in Matter. . . .

The day came when God appeared to him as the fixed and final point of convergence for an endless mounting tide of meditated and free complexification and convergence of conscious and loving spirits.

But in order to unite the Noosphere with its centre of attraction, and Matter with God, a link was needed.

A subtle, transparent, and unbreakable bond is needed between the World, human beings, and God. It must be made of indomitable but infinitely gentle energy, which not only respects beings but inspires them according to their own laws, and which respects them according to the unity of their wholeness, the law of their evolution, and their successive appearances. . . .

Could it not be that, for once, a geologist might be able to delve into something more than just the bowels of the earth? Perhaps the palaeontologist should follow another path than that leading from the past to the future? Perhaps one should dig *into* things rather than dig them out? Instead of intoxicating himself with action and the effort to transform the world, instead of amassing new treasures of knowledge through discovery, should he not rather look in perfect stillness for the Being who is? Should he not listen to the voice of all existence, and first the sound of his own existence? Supposing that instead of working he were to contemplate? This is what he once did:

"Let us penetrate our most secret selves and examine our being from all sides. Let us try at length to perceive the ocean of forces affecting us and in which our knowledge is steeped, as it were. This is a salutary exercise, for the depth and universality of our dependence will make up the embracing intimacy of our communion.

"... And so, perhaps for the first time in my life (although I am supposed to meditate every day), I took the lamp, and leaving the zone of my everyday occupations and relationships which is so clear in outward appearance, I went down into my innermost self, into the deep abyss out of which I vaguely sense that my power of action emanates. But as I moved gradually further away from the conventional certainties by which social life is superficially illuminated, I realised that I was escaping from myself. At every step downwards, a new person showed himself in me of whose exact name I could not be sure, and who no longer obeyed me. And when I had to stop my exploration because there was no more path beneath my steps, I came to a bottomless abyss out of which—from I know not where—came the stream which I venture to call *my* life.

"What science will ever be able to reveal to man the origin, nature and system of that conscious power to will and to love which make up his life? It is certainly not our own effort, nor that of anyone around us, which has caused that stream to flow. And it is not our own solicitude, nor that of any friend, which prevents it from drying up, and which controls its turbulence. We can, more or less, regularise or enlarge the aperture through which it flows into us by means of certain disciplines or stimulants. But neither by that geography nor by artifices will we succeed either in thought or practice in harnessing the sources of life. I receive of myself far more than I myself have formed. Man, according to Scripture, cannot add a cubit to his stature. Even less can he add a unit to his potential for loving, nor by another unit can he accelerate the fundamental rhythm which regulates the ripening of his mind and his heart. In the last resort, the profound life, the fontal life, the life that is being born, escapes our grasp absolutely.

"Then, excited by my discovery, I wanted to return to the light of day and forget the disquieting enigma in the comfortable surroundings of familiar things—to begin living again on the surface without imprudently plumbing the depths of the abysses. But then, beneath this very spectacle of the turbulence of human life, there reappeared before my watchful eyes the unknown from which I wanted to escape. This time, it was not hiding in the depths of an abyss but disguised itself among the innumerable strands of chance from which the stuff of the universe and my own small individuality are woven. But it was clearly the same mystery: I recognised it. Our mind is troubled when we try to measure the depth of the World below us. But it reels even more when we try to number the favourable chances whose confluence, at every moment, makes for the preservation and success of the least of living things. After the consciousness of being another and a greater than myself,—a second thing made me dizzy: the supreme improbability and the tremendous unlikelihood of finding myself existing in the heart of a world that has successfully come into being.

"I felt at that moment, like anyone else who wishes to make the same inner experiment, the typical distress of an atom lost in the universe—the distress which makes human wills founder daily under the crushing number of living things and stars. And if something has saved me, it was hearing the voice of the Gospel, guaranteed by divine successes, which said to me out of the depths of the night: '*Ego sum, noli timere* (It is I, be not afraid).'

"Yes, O God, I believe it: and I believe it all the more willingly as it is not only a question of my being comforted, but of my being completed: it is you who are at the origin of the impulse, and at the end of that pull which, all my life long, I can only follow, or whose first impulse and developments I can only favour. And it is you, also, who vivify for me, with your omnipresence (even more than my spirit can vivify the matter which it animates) the myriad influences of which I am at all times the object. In the life which springs up in me, and in the matter which sustains me, I find something even better than your gifts: it is you yourself that I find, you who make me participate in your being and who moulds me.

(. . .) "You, whose call precedes the first of our movements, grant me, O my God, the desire to desire being so that, by means of that divine thirst which you gave me, access to the great waters may open wide in me. Do not take away from me that sacred taste for being, that primordial energy, that first of our points of support (. . .)"*

And thus, at the age of forty-five, he who had once been the little boy at Sarcenat, was able to look beyond matter to see the only bond of the Whole, as illimitable as the spirit, which

* *Le Milieu divin*, 1957, pp. 74ff.

respects the identity of everything and every person, as it gathers all persons and all things together into that only Whole, outside which there is nothing.*

"Existence"—something which is not matter and which, when it is pure and total, goes infinitely beyond what we know of the mind—existence, strictly commensurate with each of us, more intimate for myself than for me, and yet universally communicated to all that is by He who is.

Existence, which is more durable than Iron, brighter than the Diamond, more communicable than Fire, is alone capable of uniting without confusing, and of establishing the harmonious accord of several which make one among realities which are the furthest removed from and the most opposed to each other.†

Why still talk of "monism" or "pantheism", since beings will not form a single whole any the less for existing as distinct individuals, and God will not be any the less close to them from the fact that he will be the unique source of being for each and every being?

Will it still be possible to speak of Omega without the name of Alpha springing to the lips?

Before being He who makes one, is he not He who makes being?

> "I am Alpha and Omega
> (The beginning and the end)
> Says the Lord God.
> 'He who is'—'He who was'—and 'He who is to come'
> THE MASTER OF ALL."
>
> *Apocalypse*, I, 8.

---

* "Everything is being, apart from the fragmentation of living creatures and the opposition of their atoms, there are only beings, everywhere" (*La Messe sur le Monde*).

† In *La Messe sur le Monde*, Teilhard writes of living creatures who are "so much suspended from the same real centre, that a true Life experienced in common gives them their definitive consistency and unification".

*Selected Writings*

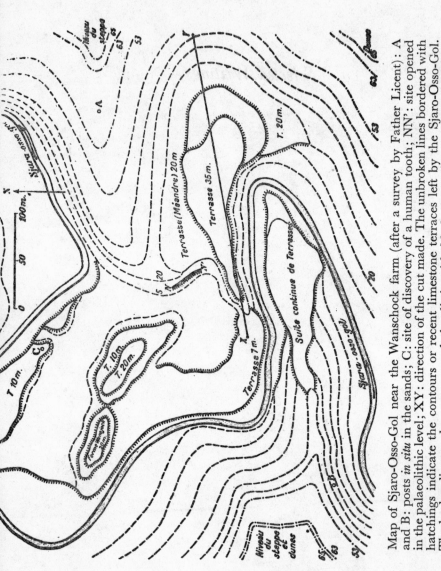

Map of Sjaro-Osso-Gol near the Wanschock farm (after a survey by Father Licent): A and B: posts *in situ* in the sands; C: site of discovery of a human tooth; NN': site opened in the palaeolithic level; XY: direction of the cut made. The unbroken lines bordered with hatchings indicate the contours or recent limestone terraces left by the Sjaro-Osso-Gol. The broken lines and —.—.—. mark the distinguishable layers projecting in the cliff-side

At dusk I climbed up the hill from which one can see the sector we have just left, and to which we will doubtless be moving up again. Before me, past the fields veiled in the rising mist, the milky-white patches marking the bends of the Aisne, I can see the barren crest of Chemin-des-Dames standing out as clearly as a knife-blade on the golden mottled slope of the *Drachen*. Far in the distance a torpedo sends up a silent spiral of smoke.

Why am I here, this evening?

In the line I am afraid of shells like everyone else. Like the others, I count the days and watch for signs that we are going to be relieved. When we "go down" I am as joyful as anyone else. And each time, it seems to me that this time, at last, I have had my fill of the trenches and the war. Only this afternoon I was still wholeheartedly savouring the joy of living again in the heart of peaceful nature, of being able to stretch myself out under the trees, and gaze up at the leaves with a mind completely at ease, in complete safety.

And here I am once more, as though by instinct, facing the front and the battle!

Is it not absurd to be so magnetised by war that I cannot spend eight days behind the lines without scanning the horizon as though it were a beloved shore, for the sight of the line of "sausages"?* To the point of not being able to spy the silver star of a falling rocket in the night, or even its reflection in the clouds, without my heart beating faster, and without feeling a regret, and a pull? . . .

In this wonderfully calm and stimulating setting, sheltered from the violent emotions and excessive tension of the trenches, I can feel all the impressions left in me by three years of war coming to life again, and feel myself more than ever spellbound by the front.

* Observation balloons, affectionately nick-named "sausages" by the French troops, because of their shape. *Transl. note.*

I passionately stare at that sacred line of hillocks of earth and bursting shells—that line of balloons who reluctantly come to rest next to each other, like two-horned extinct stars—and the line of rockets beginning to go up, as if to question it.

What then, are the properties of this fascinating and deadly line? By what secret power does it draw me, in the innermost of my being and attract me so irresistibly?

(. . .) I have the impression of having lost a soul, a soul greater than my own, which lives in the lines and which I have left there behind me.

\* \* \*

It is necessary to consider such almost mystical feelings if we are to completely explain the feelings of emptiness and disenchantment that come even after the most wished-for return to behind the lines.

The front is not only the burning crucible in which the accumulated opposing energies of the enemy are revealed and neutralised. The front is also a particular way of life, for those who risk themselves in it, which only lasts as long as one is actually in it. Once an individual has been admitted somewhere into this sublime area, it will seem certain to him that he has entered into a new way of life, which has caught hold of him.

To be sure, his individuality is safe. He will not be aware of any other centre of consciousness save that in his own soul. And yet, as soon as he has taken his place on the sacred edges of a world in activity, a new type of personality will reveal itself in him which will cover and blot out the everyday man. The man at the front is acting for the entire nation and for everything that lies hidden behind the nation. His own particular activity and passivity are being directly used in the service of an entity superior to his own in richness, duration and future. He is only secondly his own self. First and foremost, he is part of a boring-tool, part of a prow cleaving the waves. This is what he is and he feels it.

In his new and risky role the man sent under fire by his country goes accompanied by an irresistible and pacifying realisation. This man has concrete evidence that he is no longer only living for himself, that he has been delivered from himself, and that something else is living in him and dominating him. I am not afraid to say that it is this special feeling of disindividualisation which makes the combatant conscious of a human essence higher than himself, which is the ultimate secret of this incomparable feeling of freedom that he experiences and will never forget.

Let everyone observe himself as he goes up into the front line, or when in the cantonment the realisation of the next attack comes to him as a tunnel in which his whole life is to be swallowed up. A painful and perpetual process silently takes place in the realm of his emotions—a kind of detachment, brought on, inexorably, by the ever growing imminence of J-Day or H-Hour. It is not exactly melancholy, this feeling that spreads throughout everything, but rather a kind of indifference, in which the details of individual life seem distant and discoloured, while the fundamental taste for action "always", becomes ever stronger. In the citadel at Verdun, during those unforgettable days of chaos when provisions, rockets and grenades were being distributed pell-mell among the dust and cries to those who wanted to go up for the great attack,—and then, some hours later, during the interminable night march past Belleville and Froide Terre, I often noticed in myself a lacerating and victorious feeling of detachment, finally followed by a feeling of peace and exaltation among the superhuman surroundings to which the soul had become acclimatised again.

It was the soul of the front that was being re-born in me. . . .

And when one picks oneself up, covered with dust but intact, after the nearby explosion of a heavy shell, why is it that one feels this joyful swelling of the heart, this gaiety of the will, and this new perfume of life, which one never experiences when one has just escaped being run over by a train or being shot by someone careless with a revolver? Is it only the joy of having survived which lifts up the spirits of survivors from the war and which rejuvenates their world? I, myself, think that the new savour of life which comes after a *narrow escape* [in English in the original—Transl.] is due to that profound intuition that the existence one has rediscovered, consecrated by danger, is a new existence. The sense of physical well-being that suffuses the soul in those few minutes means that one had just been baptised into a new and higher kind of life. Among men he who has been under fire is a different man from the others.

Not so long ago, as I was cutting across the fields to get back to the lines (I was going past Hurtebize, which one could see burning five kilometres away) I was suddenly hailed by a peasant who accused me of going over his cultivated land. The fellow had reason to complain. But as I heard him, I felt a kind of inner shock, a giddiness, as if I were falling from very high up. . . . We both had the look of two similar beings, he and I. We spoke the same words. But he was confined within the bounds of his preoccupations as an "earthy" individualist. As for me, I was living life at the front. Who, when he has been on leave and found himself again among people and things which greet him *as of old*, has not experienced that melancholy impression of being a stranger or a freak—as if there had been an abyss between the others and oneself, only visible from one side—and precisely, not from their side?

The truth is, without this new and superhuman soul which comes to take the place of our own at the front, there would be trials and sights which would be otherwise unbearable—and yet which seem quite simple—and which still leave—this is a fact—imperishable traces of plentitude and expansion.

I affirm that for me, without the war, there would have been a world of feeling that would have remained for ever unknown to me and unsuspected by me. No one, apart from those who were there, will ever know of that memory full of wonder that men had of the plain of Ypres, in April 1915, when the air of Flanders smelt of chlorine and shells were cutting down the poplars along the river Yperie—or else of the calcined slopes of Souville in July 1916, when they smelt of death. These superhuman hours gave life a lasting, clearly defined, perfume of exaltation and initiation, as if one had spent them in the absolute.

Not all the enchantments of the Orient, not all the spiritual warmth of Paris are worth, in retrospect, the mud of Douamont.

When that peace desired by the nations (and by myself first of all) has come at last, a kind of light will suddenly go out over the Earth. War had torn open the crust of banalities and

ABOVE: June 1931, Teilhard de Chardin helping Dr. Delastre to tend a wounded Chinese soldier. BELOW: The Canyon of Sjara-Osso-God (Ordos). The cliff in the right foreground is entirely composed of pleistocene sand. To the left of the background can be seen recent tiered terraces, indicating the various stages in the hollowing-out of the canyon.

Teilhard de Chardin during a walk in the
Western Hills.

conventions. A "window" had been opened on to the secret mechanisms and deep layers of human evolution. A region was formed in which it became possible for men to breathe an air filled with the sky. With peace a veil of monotony and past meannesses will fall over all things again. As an example, around Lassigny, the area evacuated by the enemy already seems to be mournful, empty, and dispirited as the life of the front moves further on.

Happy maybe are those taken by death in the act and atmosphere of war, when they were charged and inspired by a responsibility, a consciousness and a freedom greater than any of their own, and when they were exalted on the very edge of the world—near to God!

The others, the survivors from the front will keep in their hearts a place that will be always empty and so great that nothing visible will ever be able to fill it. Let them tell themselves then, in order to conquer their nostalgia, that despite everything it is still possible for them to feel something of life at the front in themselves. Let them know it: that superhuman reality which revealed itself to them among the shell-craters and the barbed wire, will not entirely vanish in the world at peace. It will always be there even if somewhat hidden. And the world will be able to recognise it, and unite itself still with it as it devotes itself to the tasks of everyday life, no longer selfishly as before, but *religiously*, in the consciousness of fulfilling, in God and for God, the great task of creation and sanctification of a humanity which is mostly born in times of crisis, but which can only come to completion in time of peace.

* *With the army, with the sharpshooters.* September 1917. Pierre T. de. . . . (*Études*, 20 November 1917, Vol. 153, pp. 458-67).

E

## LETTERS FROM A TRAVELLER*
## IMPRESSIONS OF MONGOLIA

*On the surface, June 1923*

A few days ago we left Pao-Teo, the terminus of the railway
which, from Peking, via Kalgan and the Blue City, transports
the voyager on a more and more uncertain journey from
Europeanised and maritime China right to the Mongolian
marches. One fine evening we passed through the crenellated
walls by the Western Gate (the one used by the caravans
going to Ala-Shan and Tibet) within which the grey, flat-roofed
houses of the little city huddle together, and from there, pro-
ceeding at the pace of the ten mules which carry our explorers'
equipment, we made our way along tracks which lead to Ning-
Hia by a long detour.

Almost at once, we left behind us the first of the rocky
barriers separating the valley of the Yellow River from the
really high Asiatic plateau. On our second stage, we found
ourselves passing through the gorges of the Ula-Shan made of
garnet and white marble gneiss. Yesterday we were still at the
foot of Lang-Shan where layers of rock rose up to storm
the old crystalline shelf of China. At that moment, I must say,
the north was attracting me like a magnet. Just a few more
stages, I thought, across these grey expanses open before us—a
few more steps up this staircase of mountains, of which we have
already climbed two, and we shall come upon the solitudes of
the Gobi, the entrance to a completely mysterious land.

The course of the caravan should have been towards the
south. The goal of the journey was not, in fact, the great
Mongolian desert. We were trying to reach the Ordos region,
that little-known plateau which, to the north of Kansu and
Shensi, forms a kind of square massif, double enclosed on three

* Collected and published with a commentary by Claude Aragonnès
(Mlle Teilhard-Chambon) and published in English in *Letters from a
Traveller*, London, Collins, 1962.

of its sides, by the waters of the Hwang-Ho and a long range of mountains. If we were travelling so far to the north at that time it was only because the drought and gangs of bandits had made it impracticable for us to take the direct route across the sands.

Today, we are turning our backs on the Gobi and my eyes had already forgotten the wide torrential valleys where herds of gazelles could be seen, nose to the wind, among the pebbles and the sparse grass. We were crossing the low steppes of San-Tao-Ho.

As far as the eye could see around us, over the vast plain which had once been levelled by the Yellow River, waved the grass of the steppes, the sighi whose hard firm stalks could sometimes be as high as a man on horseback. Between its tufts, a little shrub with white flowers with fruit like pomegranate seeds which we were to taste later, formed large clusters. Now and again, some tamarisks marked an earthern hut inhabited by bronze, half-naked Chinese. The Mongolians are now no longer here. Herdsmen with the characters of children, they are gradually surrendering their ancient domain to the shrewd tenacious farmers from the east. We could scarcely see one of their yourts in the whole of the San-Tao-Ho. The season of the yellow winds was over. Sand blown from the west no longer darkened the sky, but contented itself with spinning round in little whirlwinds. We could sometimes see ten or twenty different little miniature tornadoes some fifty to a hundred metres high whirling over the steppe. I instinctively thought of the columns of smoke which used to mark the fall of some heavy shell in the plains of Flanders.

This evening, from the back of my mule, I was looking over the straw-yellow sea of sighi at the pearly-blue jagged crest of the Khara-Narim-Ula over on my right, that eastern edge of the high Mongolian plateau. And as I turned my head to the left I saw another land above the yellow sea of sighi—this time russet and purple under the rays of the setting sun. I recognised the colour at once, for I had seen it so many times from the banks of the Nile when I looked westwards towards the Red Sea. It was the colour of the burnt stones of the desert and the sand of the dunes in the dusk. It was the Ordos at last—the Promised Land.

Our tent was set in the middle of the desert, in the north-west corner of the Ordos. Around us in a large circle, some hundred metres high, curved red earth cliffs. It was very hot and all we had to drink was water drawn from a spring with salt-encrusted banks. No greenery except for some isolated tufts of strange desert plants, with woody stems and fat or prickly leaves, among which we were surprised to recognise here and there, bindweed, buckwheat or labiate—familiar plants in strange guise. Our only neighbour was a Mongol, hidden in his yourt behind a crest, two kilometres away. We were camping in the Bad Lands.

The Bad Lands have neither shade nor cool. On the other hand, as in America, their barren torn earth provides an incomparable field for the palaeontologist. In the pale layers running through the red cliffs near our camp, remains of mighty pachyderms lie pell-mell with the debris of little rodents. We spent all day bent over the white sand and a heap of treasures piled up in our tent. Pliocene fauna was abundant in the Ordos, and still is, today, in its way, judging by the fine female argali with a grey shiny coat, and as big as a small ass, which was brought back, not without some difficulty, to our camp this evening. The fawn, who is already lusty, is still running and bellowing along the edge of the cliffs.

We had not thought to open the fossil-hunting season so soon. But Mongolia is full of surprisers for the seeker. It still had more than one in store for us, this month, as we went southwards by small stages, across the Arbous-Ula to the fertile plain rich in magnificent fruits, where Musulman Ning-Hia, too small for the walls encircling it, sleeps among the rice-fields at the foot of the blue barrier of the great Ala-Shan.

Of this part of the journey, the crossing of the Arbous-Ula will remain in my memory as the finest stage. The innumerable strata of this savage mountain, a forward bastion of the Ala-Shan on the right bank of the Yellow River, bend gently into two long concentric folds which seem to unfurl over the eastern solitudes. On the broken crest of the easternmost of these waves, erosion has cut off a vast platform several miles long and wide, known to the Mongols as Genghis Khan's Anvil. Not far from the Anvil, a lamasery is tucked away on the floor of a lime-stone amphitheatre, near a spring. We asked for 1 day's hospitality there. Like all monks at all times and everywhere, the lamas showed extreme skill in choosing the setting for their dwellings. As a result it is a constant delight for the eye to suddenly light upon one of their monasteries hidden away in the most unexpected recesses. Golden flagstaffs glittered in the sun over the geometrical group of red and white rectangular buildings. Now and again a monk passed by, clad in his purple or yellow toga. Such a sight charms the eye and brings peace to the heart. Unfortunately, to admire the lamas and the lamaseries, they must be seen from afar. As soon as one goes near, the gleaming façades become tarnished, and the brightly hued garments appear dirty and torn. Those who first created these desert asylums were undoubtedly truly great men, prophets whose thought had discovered something very beautiful in the world. and beyond the world. Today, one looks anxiously but in vain for the most fleeting traces of that former vision on the dull faces of their successors.

*August*

After having crossed an interminable series of hills, covered with fragrant artemisia, liquorice trees with acacia leaves, sea-grass with horse-tail stems and strawberry-shaped fruit, we have reached the south-east corner of the Ordos, the goal of our journey. Once again, our tent was set up in the middle of the desert in a circle of earth cliffs. But here the desert was smiling, and the cliffs were grey, yellow and green instead of being red and white. We camped at the bottom of a tortuous canyon cut out of the steppes to a depth of 80 metres by the Shara-Ousso-Gol, whose liquid mud waters gurgled beside us over a stony bed.

Near us, rose the unusual dwelling that the Mongol Wanschock had dug out for himself in an islet of earth separated from the main cliff. Access to this little fortress was by an underground tunnel, and from the height of its ramparts one could survey the whole of the little alluvial plain formed at the bottom of the canyon by the river when its bed was less deep. What could bandits do against this citadel?

We owe a great deal to our friend Wanschock. It was he who welcomed us on his lands and who allowed us to excavate the layers belonging to him. Even better: it is he who has become

our best digger. We had to open a separate site for him and his
five sons. It was a curious sight to see the old Mongol sitting
by the side of the embankment, gravely inspecting excavated
fossils, carefully putting the flakes of chipped stones to one side,
and paternally directing the work of the young workers with
their bronzed torsos and long hair.

Meanwhile, the mistress of the Mongolian castle came out
of the keep, guiding her herd of flighty black goats and calm
white sheep. Like all the women around here, she wore a
helmet of coral beads with silver medals hanging down from it
over her forehead, and under this heavy headdress, which
made it impossible for her to move her head, she walked stiffly
and straightly, like an amphora-carrier. She climbed the
highest of the dunes running round the ravine like a golden
crown and there, loosening her scarf, she waved it as she sang
to herself.

We shall spend a whole month on the banks of the Shara-
Ousso-Gol, covered with lilac broom and a kind of lavender
with dark blue flowers which the Mongols incorrectly, but so
charmingly, call artemisia of argali. Between the dunes, thick
ranks of small garlic plants with pink flowers make a silken
carpet, rather like that which, I am told, brightens the melancholy Gobi at this season.

Everything smelt good and glowed cheerfully in the hot light.
The steppes are really lovely in their fleeting raiment, in the
last days of summer.

(...)

*In depth, October*

In a heavy rectangular barge which follows the eddying
current, we are going down the Hwang-Ho from Ning-Hia to
Pao-Teo. We are rapidly following, by water, the path we
followed with such difficulty four months earlier by mule. And
beyond the banks where swans, pelicans, and hundreds of
wild geese are swarming, I am trying to identify the various
stages of the outward journey.

Here are the piled-up folds of the Arbous-Ula, and then the
red desert cliffs where we killed the argali, and then the yellow
sea of sighi of the San-Tao-Ho. Here, following the Ala-Shan,
come the desolate mountain ranges encircling the Ordos: first,
the Khara-Narim-Ula running from south to north and then

the Lang-Shan, soon followed by the Ula-Shan, stretching from west to east.

As I watch these austere silhouettes pass before me in the clear light of an already cold sun, the inevitable question comes into my mind: "What am I bringing back from my four months' voyage in Mongolia? Here, around me, in the bottom of the barge, sixty cases heavy with fossils and stones were lying piled up. But this, this is all something material and external. . . . What have I gained in my innermost being during this long pilgrimage in China? What profound words has great Asia had to tell me?"

Twenty years ago, had I made this same voyage, I would have set out, I think, with the obscure hope that as I made my way over an unknown land to discover its history, I might have been able to slightly raise the curtain hiding the Great Secret from mankind. I was rather like those naïve people of Antiquity who thought that the gods inhabited the hidden regions of the world and that they especially used to show themselves to our most distant ancestors.

I have long since lost this illusion that one can approach truth through travelling. I knew it when leaving Europe: space is a seamless veil over which we can travel indefinitely without ever finding the slightest chink through which we can catch sight of the higher states of existence—and that the light we think we can see shining in the depths of the past is only a mirage or a reflection from on-high. The more the world we face is distant in time and space, the less it exists, and as a result, the poorer and more sterile it is for our thought. Thus I have felt no disappointment, this year, on not receiving the slightest strong impression, either when I looked at the steppes where gazelles ran as they did in the Tertiary period, or when I visited the yourts where the Mongols lived as they did a thousand years ago. One finds nothing really new either in that which was or in that which is.

And yet, when I landed on the shores of China, I still brought one hope with me. If, I said to myself, the exploration of space and time is only a labour in a vacuum, and if the only true knowledge of things lies in the foreseeing and gradual building up of the future as it is formed by life—what better way could I wish of initiating myself and associating myself in the building of the future than by losing myself, for weeks on end, among the fermenting mass of the peoples of Asia? There, without a doubt, I would meet the new currents of thought and mysticism as they were being formed, preparing to rejuvenate and fertilise our world of Europe. To reach full maturity the earth has need of all its blood. What could be the sap running in the old human branches of the Far East?

For long weeks I have been immersed in the deep masses of the peoples of Asia. And now, as I collect my memories and impressions together, I am obliged to confess that at the moment of emergence from this mass, my search in that direction has been vain. Nowhere, among the men I met or of whom I had heard, have I seen the smallest seed destined to grow for the future life of mankind. Throughout my voyage I have come across nothing but absence of thought, senile thought, or infantile thought. A missionary from Tibet who returned from Ko-Ko-Nor on the edges of the Himalayas, assured me that as far as he knew, two or three solitaries could still be found who nourished their inner life by contemplation of cosmic periods of time and the eternal re-birth of Buddha. But these rare heirs of a venerable tradition of thought— whose harvest is promised for some new season—are not for a passer-by like myself to recognise.

I have seen nothing in Mongolia to awaken the "other life" within me.

A pilgrim of the future, I return from a voyage made entirely in the past.

But may not the past be transformable into the future, when seen in a certain manner? Isn't a wider consciousness of that which is and that which was the essential basis of all spiritual progress? Isn't my whole life as a palaeontologist sustained by the sole hope of co-operating in a forward march? Mongolia seemed asleep to me—dead perhaps. Is there not some way of making even the dead speak?

I may have heard the secret words I had been expecting China to utter to me on the eve of my departure, while I was leaning over the battlements of the little fortified Christian outpost of Belgacoum, watching the sun set in the fiery sky of the steppe.

To my left, the smothered and fissured mountains of loess

were being softened by the sun's slanting rays. To my right, one could divine the ruins of an ancient city among the fields of buckwheat that were still pink—Si-Hia, once razed to the ground by the Mongol hordes.

And then I thought of the desperate struggle to live that had been made in these parts. In a setting hardly different from that before me, magnificent herds of animals had once sought avidly for grass and light. Next, man—a man whose remains lie buried sixty metres under the sand near the Shara-Ousso-Gol —had battled against elements that were still incomprehensible and savage. Much later, Genghis Khan had crossed this plain in all the pride of his victories.

And today, of all this tremendous thrust towards a little more life, nothing remains—nothing but a few poor fields painfully struggling against the encroaching sands. . . .

Nothing?

I watched the golden star as it sank behind the dunes, taking with it all the infinite range of colours in nature. And then it seemed that before me it was no longer the fiery sun that I saw settling over the Mongolian desert, but the very hearth of Terrestrial Life which was to rise again *in our part of the world.*

And from the whole of Asia sleeping in the night I thought I heard a voice which whispered: "Now, brothers of the West, it is your turn!"

Our turn. Yes, sleep on, ancient Asia, you whose peoples are as weary as your soil is ravaged. At this hour night has fallen and the light has passed into other hands. But this light—it was you who lit it and who gave it to us. Have no fear, we will not let it go out. Your labour will not have been in vain. Moreover, sheltered in the hearts of a few wise men as it is, your life (your own life—not that which we would seek to impose on you) is not extinct. It will shine again tomorrow, perhaps, over your worn plateau.

Our turn. Yes, this I believe more than ever.

The sceptics, the agnostics, the false positivists are wrong. Throughout all the civilisations which have succeeded one another, the world is neither moving at hazard nor marking time but, beneath the universal turmoil of living beings, something is being prepared, something celestial doubtless, but first something temporal. Nothing is lost of his struggle to man down here. Persuaded as I am that the only true science is that which discovers the growth of the universe, I was worried because I found nothing in my travels but the traces of a vanished world. But why should I be worried? Does the wake left behind by a mankind marching forward reveal its movement to us any less clearly than the spray thrown back by the prow of peoples thrusting onwards?

This evening, as I watched the play of gold and red clouds above the river and the flight of wild geese silhouetted in black against them I told myself again: the hour when we must look at the Far East, if we wish to understand it, is not that of dawn or high noon—it is at the hour of dusk when the sun, bearing the spoils of Asia with it in its glory, rises in triumph over the skies of Europe.

(*Yellow River*, October 1923)

The National Geological
   Survey of China,          *9 Ping Ma Seu West City,*
     Peiping (China).            *February 4th, 1934.*

My Reverend Father,

    I have just read your precious little book *Dieu ou Rien* [God or nothing] which has just landed on our far-off shores. Allow me to communicate the joy it gave me. With your voice, so measured and so full of authority, you have begun at last to speak the words which I had so long dreamed of hearing ringing out frankly in the Church. I am convinced that if Christianity has often had so much trouble in keeping its true place in the minds of believers, and also in winning the souls of the Gentiles, it is mainly because it sometimes gives the impression of scorning or fearing the grandeur and unity of our universe. At last, in your pages, one can feel a wholly un-feigned and passionate sense of sympathy for the work of the world, a spirit of God nourished by the spirit of the earth. This is what we have been waiting for. I often think that, for our humanity which has certainly become more adult now than it was two thousand years ago, what is needed in some sort, is a "renaissance" of Christ, a Christ reincarnating Him-self, for the sake of our intelligence and our hearts, in the tremendous dimensions that have recently been discovered in the experimental Real. Our Christ must be capable of covering and lighting up these almost immeasurable extensions. *Neque longitudo, neque latitudo, neque profundum* . . . I imagine that St. Thomas recognises himself in the joyful audacity with which you see them widening a little more, day by day, before us. It is good to feel that one has such companions-in-arms around one in the Church.

    Please believe me to be yours very respectfully, faithfully, devotedly, etc.

DURING the last ten years prehistoric discovery has been continuing at a steady rate without any signs of slackening, without attracting the attention of the general public, because it has been doing so gradually and always in the same direction. Our knowledge of "fossil-men" is at present increasing so rapidly that today there is not one really up-to-date scientific text-book on human origins.

Two kinds of data characterise the latest results obtained in the field of human palaeontology. First, the discovery of several human types which confirm the reality and complexity of a "neanderthaloid"* stage in the evolution of man: the Steinheim skull (Germany), the Saccopastore skulls (Rome), the skeletons found in Palestine, the Javanese Ngandong skulls (Homo soloensis), and recently, the Tanganyika skull. Finally, the discovery of "Peking Man" or Sinanthropus, which has decisively proved the existence—which had been foreseen but not yet proved—of a pre-Neanderthaloid phase of humanity.

It is this last discovery that I would now like to sum up, in my capacity as an eye-witness.

A. *Origins of the discovery of the Sinanthropus.*

As always in palaeontology, the discovery of the Sinanthropus was due to a methodically exploited hazard. Let us first list the facts:

In about 1921, Doctor J. G. Andersson, adviser to the Geological Service of China, had his attention drawn to a fossil bearing fissure at Chou-Kou-Tien near Peking, and had it excavated for some time by his colleague, Doctor O. Zdansky. Among the bones excavated (which showed that the deposits in the fissure were of a very great age), Zdansky noticed two teeth of a human appearance and announced the find in 1926.

* This is the rather conventional name we give to the phase represented in Western Europe by the classic Neanderthal Man (Chapelle-aux-Saints Man), an archaic type who was suddenly replaced in our grottoes by the *homo sapiens* cave painters of the Reindeer (Cro-Magnon) Age towards the middle of the last Ice Age.

Immediately realising the importance of the find, the late Doctor Davidson Black, professor of anatomy at the Peking Medical College (Rockefeller Foundation), decided upon an exhaustive investigation of the site in agreement with Doctor W. H. Wong, the director of the Geological Survey of China. Lavishly subsidised by the Rockefeller Foundation, the work began immediately (1927).

Such were the beginnings of an enterprise which has been continuing without interruption for ten years, on an unparalleled scale in the annals of prehistoric research,* and which has gradually resulted in the emergence of the astonishing figure of the Sinanthropus out of the depths of the past.

## B. *The site of Chou-Kou-Tien.*

The site of the excavations at Chou-Kou-Tien lies some thirty miles to the south-west of Peking in a cluster of small calcareous hills bordering the mountain chain forming the western edge of the maritime plain of northern China. As is often the case the limestone of the hills has been hollowed out inside into numerous pockets, formed in geological times by the action of underground waters. Empty, or else recently filled in with fallen rocks, sand and red clay-stone, these pockets are generally indistinguishable among the rounded grassy slopes of the hills. But, fortunately for palaeontologists, a continuing line of quarries cut in order to extract limestone has brought them to light, one after another, in the course of exploitation. A red window opening in a hard bluish wall of rock: this was how the fissure, crammed with fossils and soon destined to become famous under the name of "Locality 1" at Chou-Kou-Tien, first appeared to the disappointed quarrymen.

When Doctor Andersson saw it for the first time, in front of the quarry which had been dug by it, it seemed that Locality 1 might only be a deposit of modest size and from the very beginning it needed all Davidson Black's enthusiasm to mobilise the most powerful equipment to attack the site.

* Excavations, in which as many as a hundred workers are employed on the site, are carried out for eight months every year. The material collected is prepared and studied the whole year round in Peking, in two laboratories, and descriptions regularly appear in the publications of the Geological Survey of China. See especially, the *memoire, Fossil Man in China*, written by Dr. Black and myself, and published in *Memoires of the Geological Survey of China.*

But his optimism was justified beyond the wildest expectations. As we now know it the Sinanthropus bed contains an almost inexhaustible supply of deposits, in a layer more than a hundred metres long, with an average width of thirty metres, *and a depth* of more than fifty metres: the most important accumulation of archaeological deposits ever made in prehistory! How could such a hoard be explained?

In the course of the excavations at Chou-Kou-Tien, it was first thought that Locality 1 represented an ancient vertical split which had been gradually filled by material coming from outside: the bones which were found mixed with the stones would then have been those of animals who had accidentally fallen into the natural trap. But as better known deposits were inspected another hypothesis was gradually formed and has now become generally accepted: namely that the site corresponds to a former cavern which was more or less ramified, had become progressively larger, and at the same time become filled up due to the continuous caving-in of the roof. This second interpretation is clearly borne out by the structure of the deposits, where the finer layers especially rich in "cultural" remains and bones (periods of habitation by men or animals) regularly alternated with thick beds of fallen rock (periods of abandonment and cavings-in). Moreover, nothing is left today of the vault of the grotto. Destroyed by erosion, the last traces of the roof must have vanished long before the present period. At present the fossil-bearing breccia of Locality 1, reshaped and rounded until they have become joined in the confining limestone towards the end of the Quaternary period, have become a part of the hill itself: one of many proofs of their great age.

It is in this imposing mass of debris, sometimes barely consolidated, but more often so firmly cemented together by infiltrating waters that they have had to be cleared by explosives, that were found the animal and human remains which we must now describe.

## C. *Palaeontological results of the excavations.*

Apart from the remains of the Sinanthropus, which we shall shortly describe, an enormous mass of fossil animals has been found buried in the Chou-Kou-Tien ossuary. This evidence is clearly of great value in helping us to determine the age of the site. Among this fauna, mostly comprising extinct species, two main groups can be distinguished: that of the animals who lived in the cavern, and that of their prey.

The first group (not including Man) comprises: an extremely large but very common type of hyena, large feline fauna (tiger, panther, and more exceptionally, the *Machairodus*, or sabre-toothed tiger), a large and a small bear, etc.

The second group, mainly indicated by broken limbs and skulls, consists of: an ostrich, a large horse, two species of rhinoceros, an elephant, a very large camel, an antelope with spiral horns, buffalo, wild sheep, and a considerable number of deer, some resembling the *sika* of the present day, others resembling the *Megaceros* of Quaternary Europe, but with shorter and more widely set antlers and monstrously thick facial bones.

Together with other physiographic and lithographic evidence, palaeontological study of this material confirms that the filling up of the cavern took place in a remote Quaternary period. In this far-off period, some hundred thousand years ago, Northern China, which had recently been raised up by a movement of the Asiatic shelf, was covered by heavy rubefied alluvia which was, in its turn, destined at a geological date to be covered by a thick mantle of grey loess.

Such is the site, impressive by its great age, where we encountered the Man of the red earth of China, the Sinanthropus.

## D. *The remains of the Sinanthropus.*

The exceptional interest of such a cave-deposit to the prehistorian is due to the fact that such a deposit permits us to catch man *at home*, that is, in a kind of concentrated state. It is only by an extraordinary chance that human bones are ever found in the old gravel beds of a river. In an ancient site of habitation, on the contrary, the chances of making such a discovery are naturally much greater. These favourable circumstances allow one to explain the important number of Sinanthropus remains which have been gathered over the last ten years in the Chou-Kou-Tien fissure. In this category, we now have, at the present:

Five almost complete skulls (the facial structure is incomplete), of which the three last, all adults, were found in December 1936.

Important fragments of three other skulls.

Some ten more or less complete jaw-bones (young and adult).
A greater number of individual teeth.

The whole representing some thirty individual specimens.

One curious thing: the anatomical characteristics of these numerous specimens (as well as the type of fauna associated with them) have not undergone any noticeable change corresponding to the different depths in which they were found in the layer, which would indicate that the whole layer must have been formed in the same geological period.

And, even more curious: no part of a skeleton has yet been found apart from the above-mentioned skulls and parts of skulls, except for an atlas, a clavicle, and a fragment of a humerus. Heads, practically nothing but heads. We shall come back to this enigmatic circumstance.

Another important fact: from the surface down to the deepest layers of the deposit the remains of the Sinantropus are found corresponding to well defined cultural levels, containing an abundance of ash, calcined and broken bones, and rather summarily but still clearly worked stones.

What anthropological conclusions are to be made from an analysis of these varied remains?

E. *The anatomical characteristics of the Sinanthropus.*

Thanks to the considerable number of specimens, both young and old, that we now have at our disposal, the Sinanthropus is (at least as far as concerns the skull) one of the fossilmen who has been the best identified today by human palaeontology. The studies made of him to date by Doctor Black and his successor Doctor Weidenreich have resulted in the acceptance by the greater part of the anthropological world of a certain number of major conclusions, which can be listed as follows:

The Sinanthropus is, anatomically speaking, a member of the human zoological group—a "Hominien". This is proved notably by the general contours of the jaw-bone, the shape and sizes of the premolar and canine teeth, and even more by the cranial capacities, which range from nine hundred to twelve hundred cubic centimetres.

But at the same time the Sinanthropus distinguishes himself from all the other known fossil-men by a number of important cranial features: the vault of the skull is very low; the skull attains its maximum width at the level of the ear-openings and not above them (which results in a transversal section of the skull having a curved and not an ovoid shape); the maximum length of the skull is between the base of the nose and a strongly defined occipital ridge (instead of being between the base of the nose and the protuberance which, in present and Neanderthal man, overhangs the occipital ridge). Moreover the suborbital ridges are powerful and prominent, and followed posteriorly by a constriction which is much more marked than in men of the Neanderthal group. The teeth have very long roots without any well defined neck under the crown. Very strong canines in the male. No sign of a chin. No canine fossa, etc. Absolutely nothing, to be sure, to indicate a "degenerate" type!

By virtue of its fundamental characteristics a Sinanthropus skull can be placed morphologically, roughly as far below the Neanderthaloid group as the latter below the modern, superior, palaeolithic group of *Homo sapiens*. To a very approximate degree of precision, usually not surpassed by our palaeontological series, only one last theoretical rung has to be put in after Peking Man for the evolutionary ladder to be practically complete (as far as regards the skull) as it leads from the anthropoid to the human species.

At this point, a question remains to be answered: being so far removed from present man by the formation of its skull, can the Sinanthropus be considered as an intelligent being?

### F. *The intelligence of the Sinanthropus.*

At first sight the question as to whether the Sinanthropus was a thinking being seems to have been immediately and positively answered by the fact of the conditions of its "environment". Fire, and tools, on one hand, and the manifestly intentional selection of the skulls we have found on the other, seem to answer our question. Are not proofs of intelligence to be found in abundance in the Chou-Kou-Tien deposits?

Naturally a certain number of palaeontologists will reply, following Professor M. Boule: there was indeed an intelligent being among the denizens of the cavern—a Man in the fullest sense of the word. We are not contesting this. But can you be sure that this man was the Sinanthropus himself and not another more evolved species? All you find of the Sinanthropus are his skulls. These remains could not have belonged to the actual inhabitant of the grotto, but must have been brought by him into his lair as trophies or for some other reason, as were the animal remains littering the site you have been exploring. No, nothing proves that the Sinanthropus, whose primitive state is attested by the form of his skull, could have been capable of the kinds of activity you have attributed to him.

I must confess that it is rather difficult to answer this specious objection with any immediate proof. To remark that no traces of the bones of this hypothetical man have been found at Chou-Kou-Tien is not a wholly satisfactory reply. We know of many prehistoric sites in Europe where the deposits of ashes and flints have never yielded up any trace of former inhabitants. In theory the same phenomenon could very well have occurred at Chou-Kou-Tien. As so often happens in the purely retrospective sciences of the past, it would seem then that up to a certain point we will have to resign ourselves to affirming that the Sinanthropus was intelligent, with certain reservations, while waiting for additional information that excavations may provide at a later date.

But—and this is what Doctor Weidenreich, the Abbé Breuil and many others think, following Davidson Black's theories—it must be admitted that despite M. Boule's subtle observations, this intelligence appears as the most simple and likely hypothesis in the light of the facts that have come to light. As we have said, by its anatomical characteristics the Sinanthropus is decidedly part of the human family tree. Among the last three skulls found in December 1936, one (that belonging to a large male) was found to have a capacity of twelve hundred cubic centimetres. Why then in these conditions should we seek to contest the positive evidence provided by these excavations by imagining the existence of another worker-human being? . . . Without going as far as P. W. Schmidt's really extreme view, according to which there was a quasi-religious arrangement in the way the Chou-Kou-Tien skulls were placed (the skulls were found carelessly crushed and scattered among remains of cooking!) it would seem that the wisest thing to do, given the present state of investigations, would be to regard Peking Man as a being in whom the flame of thought had already, and doubtless for a long time, been lit—as a *Homo faber* already, walking erect and using his hands as we do.

Once we have agreed on this point, the anthropological place of the Sinanthropus becomes clear enough. Together with his brother or his cousin, the Java Pithecanthropus, he represents a very old human group of the lower Quaternary period, localised in south-east Asia—a backward group, possibly, and consequently one that may have been contemporary with other more progressive species such as Chellean Man (that unknown . . .) of Africa and western Europe, but decidedly still a member of the great human family. Having arrived at the following "Neanderthaloid" stage, this group would seem to have produced Ngandong Man (Java Man) during the late Quaternary period. After this he would have disappeared, being either effaced or absorbed by younger and more active forms of humanity.

This, in brief, is what we know of the Sinanthropus at the present moment. The excavations at Chou-Kou-Tien will go on for several years and doubtless will provide new information. Meanwhile it is useless to insist on the definitive interest of the results so far obtained.

These results evidently bring confirmation—at least of a general nature—for transformist views on the origins of the human species. But, otherwise, let us insist clearly on this point —they do nothing to disprove a spiritual conception of humanity—far from it. At the same time that he digs ever deeper into the remote past with the aid of prehistory, man tends to take a preponderating place among the achievements of modern science, thanks to his unique qualities: his psychic, individual and social energies appear, to an ever increasing extent, to the physicist as much as to the biologist, as one of the great forces of the universe. Are there not two complementary ways for the spirit to dominate everything and to fill everything? Thought would not be the ruler of the world if it did not hold, by every thread, even the humblest elements of matter.

For he who knows how to see, by binding Man more closely to the earth the discovery of the Sinanthropus is nothing less than one more feature adding to the supreme importance in nature of the "phenomenon of man".

(*Études*, July 5th, 1937).

# TEILHARD DE CHARDIN'S THOUGHT AS WRITTEN BY HIMSELF

*for an article which was to have been devoted to him*

ESSENTIALLY, Teilhard de Chardin's thought does not express itself in metaphysics but in a kind of phenomenology. He believes that a certain law of recurrence, which creates and dominates all experience, can be observed by us: a law of complexification—consciousness by virtue of which, in the interior of life, cosmic matter coils more and more closely in on itself, following a process of arrangement, measured by a correlative increase of tension (or psychic temperature). In the field of our observation *reflecting Man* represents the highest elementary factor in this movement towards arrangement. But this coiling process prolongs itself beyond individual man in Humanity by means of the social phenomenon, at the end of which a superior critical glimpse of collective reflection may be perceived.

From this point of view, "hominisation" (socialisation included) is a converging phenomenon (i.e. presenting a superior limit, or an inner point of maturation). But, by its structure, this phenomenon of *convergence* is inherently *irreversible*, in the sense that, when Evolution has become reflected and free in man, it cannot continue its ascending progress towards complexification-consciousness without recognising that the "vital coiling" not only goes onwards to escape total annihilation or death, but also gathers together all the preservable essence of what life has engendered during its progress. This insistence on irreversibility implies from the structural point of view the existence of a transcending centre of unification, the "Omega point", at the superior final point of cosmic convergence. Without this irreversibilising, gathering, focal point, it is impossible to preserve the law of evolutionary recurrence to the very end.

It is on the basis of these "Physics" that Father Teilhard has, in a second phase, built up:

1. First, an Apologetic: under the illuminating influence of grace, our spirit recognises a manifestation (reflection) of the Omega on human consciousness and in the unifying properties of the Christian phenomenon, and it identifies the Omega of reason with the Universal Christ of revelation.

2. A *mystique*, at the same time: as the whole of evolution finds itself brought back to a process of union (of communion) with God, so it becomes integrally loving and lovable in the most intimate and terminal of its developments.

Taken together, the three branches of the system (physics, apologetic and *mystique*) easily suggest and outline a Metaphysic of Union, dominated by love, and in which even the problem of evil finds a plausible intellectual solution (static necessity of disorders inside a multitude in the process of arrangement).

This "philosophy" has been reproached with being only a kind of generalised concordism. In reply to this criticism Father Teilhard declares that concordism and coherence must not be confused. In the mental sphere it is evident that religion and science represent two different meridians which it would be wrong not to separate (concordist error). But these meridians must necessarily meet at some point in a pole of common vision (coherence): otherwise everything in the domain of thought and knowledge will collapse within us.

*April 1948*                                              N.Y.
(Review *Les Études philosophiques*
October-December 1955—new series, 10th year, no. 4.)

THE HUMAN ZOOLOGICAL GROUP

*Evolutionary Structure and Course**

## I

THE PLACE AND MEANING OF LIFE IN THE UNIVERSE
A WORLD COILING ON ITSELF

(...)

### Diverse Forms of Arrangement of Matter
### "True" and "False" Complexity

WHEN, in what follows, I use the word *complexity*, I do not of
course mean *simple aggregation*, i.e. a random assembly of
*unarranged* elements such as a pile of sand, or even such elements
(excluding a certain zonal classification due to gravity, no
matter what might be the multiplicity of the substance composing it) as the stars and planets.

By this word neither do I mean the simple geometrical,
indefinite *repetition* of unity (no matter how varied, or numerous
the axis of their arrangement)—as it occurs in the astonishing
and universal phenomenon of crystallisation.

The precise meaning in which I use this word is *combination*,
i.e. this particular and higher form of arrangement whose
characteristic is to bind a certain, fixed, number of elements
(few or many—no matter) to itself, with or without the auxili-
ary help of aggregation or repetition, in a closed mass of determined radius, such as the atom, the molecule, the cell, the
metazoan, etc . . .

A fixed number of elements—a closed mass. Let us insist on
this double characteristic on which, in fact, depends the entire
succession of these developments.

In the case of aggregation and crystallisation, by its very
nature the arrangement is, and constantly remains, exteriorly
uncompleted. Therefore a new addition of matter from outside

* Published by Éditions Albin Michel, 1956.

is always possible. In other words, in the star or the crystal there is no trace of a unification limited in relation to itself, but only the simple apparition of an accidentally "outlined" system.

Combination, on the contrary, creates a type of group which is structurally complete in itself at each instant (although starting with a certain type we shall see,* they can be indefinitely extensible inside themselves): the *corpuscule* (micro- or mega-corpuscule), a unity which is truly and doubly "natural" in the sense that, organically limited in its outlines in relation to itself, it also shows precise phenomena of *autonomy* at certain higher levels of internal intricacy. A complexity which progressively gives rise to a certain "centreity", not of symmetry but of action. To put it more briefly and precisely one might call it "centro-complexity".†

*Dynamism of Corpusculisation*
*Expansion of Consciousness*

As our minds gradually escape from the limitations and stability of the ancient conception of the Cosmos, we begin to get used to the idea of major currents affecting the universe in its totality. First, regressive currents of which the first to be recognised were Entropy and disaggregation of energy. But there are also progressive and constructive currents. Do we not now speak of "exploding universe", starting from some former "atom" in which Time and Space annihilated themselves in a sort of absolute zero?

It is on this scale and in this style, if I am not mistaken, that we must think of life if we are to understand Man.

After all, the idea of a Universe expanding in space to explain why the spectrum of galaxies turns red is all very well, and nobody objects to it.

But why not then, in order to make the persistent, insistent, ubiquitous mechanism of Corpusculisation comprehensible— why not a Universe which, all together, from top to bottom, coils in upon itself until it interiorises itself in growing complexity? . . .

I know it and I feel it. Impressed as we are by what seems

* The class of the "living corpuscules" (Author's note).
† pp. 16-18 (Editor's note).

improbable in the formation of higher living complexes in the light of the old determinist science, we instinctively recoil from simultaneously including them all in a scientific system of defined "causality". The idea of something exceptional or abnormal always crops up whenever it is a question of constructing a science of the Physics or arrangement. And yet do not the facts—an ever growing accumulation of facts—oblige us to admit that:

"abandoned to itself, undeniably, a part of the Cosmic stuff not only does not disaggregate, but, by a kind of flowering process, even starts to vitalise. So much that, besides Entropy (by which energy is degraded), besides Expansion (by which the layers of the Universe unfurl themselves and become granulous), and besides electric and gravitational attractions (which cause sideral dust to agglomerate), we are henceforth obliged (if we really want to complete the experiment and save *all* the phenomenon) to consider and admit the existence of a constant, perennial current of 'interiorising complexification' animating the total mass of Things."

Here, then, we have gained a first point. Independently of any scientific (and even less finalist) interpretation on our part, the Universe falls from above into ever more perfected patterns of arrangement.

But sudden realisation is not enough to satisfy our minds, which are insatiably avid to understand everything thoroughly. The existence of a cosmic, self-coiling movement certainly seems to be incontestable. But where should we look for its inner spring?*

In the rest of this work it will become clear, I hope, (. . .) that if, until the coming of Man, only the determinist spring of pure natural selection can at a pinch suffice to give an exterior idea of the progress of Life, once we come to the "Steps of Reflection", at least, it will be necessary to add (or even to substitute) the psychic spring of invention if we wish to explain, even in its higher limits, the ascending path of cosmic Corpusculisation.

On this point, doubtless, Science has yet to say its last word.

* pp. 33-5 (Editor's note).

It remains, at least, in every case (and this, really, is the only question that matters here) that if our world is really in course of arrangement in one way or another, then it will be easier for us to understand that life in the universe can no longer be regarded as a superficial accident. Instead we must consider it as being held in bounds everywhere, ready to burst out anywhere in the cosmos through the slightest crack, and, once having appeared, as being incapable of not making the most of every opportunity and every means to reach the extreme limit of its capabilities, producing complexification on the exterior and Consciousness in the interior.

It is this which makes the study of Man and his Genesis, on which we are about to embark, so fundamental and so dramatic.

Man: not merely a Zoological species like others, but as the nucleus of a coiling and converging movement which, on our little planet (lost as it is in Time and Space), shows itself as what is probably the most characteristic and revealing drift in the immensities enveloping us.

Man: it is he around whom and in whom the Universe is coiling itself.*

## II

### THE SPREADING OF THE BIOSPHERE
### AND THE SEGREGATION OF THE ANTHROPOIDS

A. *The choice of a new parameter for Evolution: coefficient of complexification and nervous system.*

(...)

That which defines and measures the coiling of the universe at every point and at every moment is, by definition, the degree of vitalisation attained by matter at the point and summit already mentioned. But this is not all. We must add that: that which again defines and measures the vitalisation of any given corpuscle is its degree of interiorisation or "psychic temperature" (consciousness, which in man culminates in freedom). Since, as we have admitted, (...) the two variables are closely related, what is there to say except that: if, by any chance, there was a certain portion (or organ) in the living

* pp. 37-38 (Editor's note).

being which was more specially related to its psychic development, it was the complexity of this part, and this part only (the
rest will only confuse the measures!) which could, and should,
be used in order to appreciate the degree of corpusculisation
reached by the living being under examination.

Have I not, in fact, been describing the *nervous system*?

The variation of the nervous system—or to put it still more
precisely, the variation of its cephalised part—or even more
simply and in a word—the *Cephalisation*, is the conductor-wire
we need! Geneticians have necessarily found themselves
obliged to separate the *soma* from the *germen* in Metazoary
bodies, the latter having the sole responsibility for the trans-
mission of hereditary characteristics. Similarly, and perhaps
even more deservedly, we are now led to distinguish the *soma*
from the "*phren*",* the first being without interest and the latter
being of decisive importance when we have to measure the
degree of vitalisation of living beings. From this point of view,
which has been largely amended and made more precise, the
number of molecules involved in the skeleton or muscular
system of an animal is of little importance. Just as unimportant
(up to a certain point) is the gross volume of its brain. But the
only thing that finally counts in the absolute classification† of
higher forms of life is (apart from the number) the perfection
of the structure and functioning of their cerebral neurones.

It will be said that this is still a very undecipherable (or at
least very "un-cipherable") parameter! But it is very useful,
in so far as it is expressed concretely in certain precise morphological characteristics, as we shall see—such as the coiling, the
concentration and the selective development of such or such a
part of the brain.

Let us rather see how, by application of this criterion (made
gradually more precise) of cephalisation or cerebralisation, the
confused arborescence of a crowd of living beings finally
clarifies and arranges itself, and finally leaps forward at one
stroke along a single main stem.

B. *First result obtained by application of the parameter of cerebralisa-*

---

\* From a Greek word designating the (supposed) organ of psychic life
(originally and literally the enveloping substance around the liver or the
heart). (Author's note.)

† i.e. by order of "complexification". (Author's note.)

*tion: the main axis of the cosmic coiling (or corpusculising) process on Earth lies in the branch of mammiferous beings.**

C. *Second result obtained by application of the parameter of cerebralisation: the terrestrial axis of corpusculisation passes through the order of Primates, and more precisely, the family of Anthropoids.*†

D. *The Pliocene "Anthropoid task" in the Biosphere.*

(. . .)

Reduced to essentials, this bio-geographical history can be divided into the five phases as follows:

a. *First appearance in the lower Eocene period,* on a vast block of land which comprised North America and Western Europe simultaneously—the two regions then apparently being connected by some sort of north-Atlantic bridge.‡ Very small living forms (scarcely larger than a mouse), of which certain were decidedly "tarsoidal" (Anaptomorphidae). It would obviously be extremely useful to know what was happening at the same period in the south of Tethys. Unfortunately we still do not know of any continental fossil-bearing deposit in Africa for this period.

b. *Increase in size and numbers during the middle Eocene period.* In appearance, general conditions (zoological as much as geographical) have undergone little change for the Primates: the same species (Lemuroids and Tarsoids) are found throughout the same region. And yet profound changes are certainly taking place or being about to take place. On one hand, it seems that the transatlantic bridge has already been severed, and on the other hand, South America is being invaded—as proved by the conditions found at the start of the following phase.

c. *Separation and radical transformation of the group in the Oligocene period.* Definitively nothing more in North America, and only the mere survival of some Lemuroids in Western Europe. By contrast, establishment of a *platyrrhinian* block in South America, and emergence in Africa (Fayum) of an extremely vigorous centre of evolution (an autochthonous hearth of life rather than one set alight by sparks blown over from Europe): apparition of the *first Anthropoids.*

---

\* pp. 56-8 (Editor's note).
† p. 66 (Editor's note).
‡ A much more likely hypothesis than that of trans-Asiatic communications for which there is absolutely no palaeontological proof. (Author's note.)

d. *Miocene expansion of the Anthropoids.* Starting from its African (and more probably central African,—Kenyan) hearth the wave of "anthropoids", led by Dryopithecedae, spreads widely over all the southern edges of Eurasia at this epoch. In the west, going above a largely saturated Tethys, it reaches Spain, France, and southern Germany. In the east, although we still have no direct proofs, it extended in all likelihood as far as the Pacific (without ever going beyond the Himalayas and the Yangtse in the north), to the edge of the Indian Ocean. Afterwards, in the western sector, the wave retreated to the south of the Mediterranean as we now know it—while consolidating itself and taking roots at other points, the whole operation resulting in what one might call:

e. *The Pliocene establishment of an anthropoid sector.* In nature at present the great humanoid monkeys (Gorilla, Chimpanzee, Gibbon, Orang-Outang) only form a disconnected series of islets stretching from Gabon to Borneo. From the end of the trertiary period man has made his appearance there. By con-Tast, if we take into account the distribution and frequency of fossils known to us, we must visualise a dense and continuous wave of varied (and actively mutating) Anthropoids covering a large tropical and sub-tropical zone reaching from the Atlantic to the Pacific. Teeth and mandibles of varied Anthropoids are relatively common in the sub-Himalayan deposits of this period, and we know that the Orang-Outang was swarming throughout Southern China and Indo-China at the beginning of the Quaternary period.*

# III

## THE APPARITION OF MAN:
## OR THE PROGRESS OF REFLECTION

(. . .)

*Hominisation: A mutation differing from all others in its developments*

By the fact that we are men, living among other men, we end by no longer being able to appreciate the true grandeur of the human phenomenon.

* pp. 69-71 (Editor's note).

Naturally this observation will especially apply for the next two chapters devoted to the "planetary" phases of hominisation. But it is already relevant here inasmuch as we are already faced with the surprising zoological fact that, from the end of the Tertiary period onwards, the Earth's main evolutionary efforts are visibly concentrated in man.

How can we deny the evidence that, since the Pliocene period, the best that remained of the sap of life seems to have been concentrated in Man? In the course of the last two million years we can observe the disappearance of a great many species in nature and not one single really new manifestation of life, apart from that of Man. In itself this symptomatic fact should draw our attention and excite our suspicions. But why not now pass to a more detailed analysis of the phenomenon? What drive, what exuberance and what originality there is in this last-born of the children of the Earth! A typical case of mutation: this is how we have already defined and labelled the apparition of Man at the centre of the "anthropoid endeavour" during the Pliocene period. Yes, no doubt. But on condition that we add that this was a *unique* mutation *of its kind*, due to the fact that in this phylum to which it gave birth, four properties (exceptional by virtue of their intensity, or even decidedly singular in their novelty) make their appearance from the very beginning. These four properties, which we must study in succession, are as follows:

An extraordinary power of expansion.
Extreme rapidity of differentiation.
An unexpected persistence in the power of germination.
And lastly, the capacity—hitherto unknown in the history of life—for inter-liaison among different branches of the same tree.

## IV

### THE FORMATION OF THE NOOSPHERE

A. *The Socialisation of Expansion. Civilisation and Individuation.* (. . .)

Finally, at the point we have come to so far in this *exposé*, the situation with regard to the World in course of corpuscular arrangement can be described as follows: due to the break-through of hominisation, the wave of complexification-consciousness following the Anthropoid phylum has made its way on the Earth into a domain or compartment which is absolutely new to the Universe: that of Reflection. And, once having taken this leap forward, this wave had begun again to diffract itself into a complicated pencil of more or less diverging rays (as in the past each time it had to pierce through yet another ceiling): the various zoological radiations from the human group. But, as we have seen at the end of the last chapter, because these rays henceforth propagate themselves in a psychically convergent milieu, they have rapidly shown a marked tendency to come together and join up among themselves. And it is thus that the eminently progressive group of *Homo sapiens* was born in an atmosphere of (or due to) socialisation.

In the light of all evidence, the socialisation (or association in symbiosis with psychic liaisons of histologically free corpuscles) indicates a primary and universal property of vitalised matter.* To be convinced of this, it is enough to observe how each family of animals (in proportion to its "type of instinct" and according to the particular modalities of this latter), once it has reached a specific point of maturity, shows a tendency for a more or less large number of the elements composing it to group themselves in the form of supra-individual complexes. Nevertheless, at these pre-reflected levels (especially with regard to Insects), the ray of socialisation (no matter how strong) emitted always remains very feeble, never going beyond the family group, for example. We may say therefore that the advent of Man opens a new chapter in the history of zoology, when, for the first time in the annals of Life, it is no longer a few isolated leaves but an entire—and even better—a ubiquitous phylum which suddenly gives the impression of totalising itself *en bloc*. Man, who has appeared as a simple species, has gradually come to form a specifically new layer enveloping the earth by a process of ethnico-social unification. More than an off-shoot, more than even a Reign, it is neither more nor less than a "sphere"—the

---

* Already recognisable by the inferior degrees of autonomy in the element, in the formation of animal (Polyps, etc.) or even Metazoary (associated cells) colonies. (Author's note.)

La règle qui me dirige est la suivante : pas d'erreur substantielle à craindre si mon attitude intérieure a bon résultat de me rendre plus fidèle, plus attentif, plus passionnément intéressé aux hommes et à la tâche humaine, — mais dépendant, en même temps, de moi-même également. En transposant cette règle un peu plus haut, il me semble que vous ne risquez rien tant que l'esprit qui vous porte vous rendra plus vivant humainement (au beau sens du mot), et en même temps plus attaché à ce qui fait l'essence du Christ : sa personnalité physiquement réelle, sa divinité, sa manifestation dans et par l'Eglise. — Ce qui rend la "haute" mystique dangereuse, ce sont les écarts qui lui font perdre de vue (précisément à l'encontre de ce que vous tenez) la Matière, — c.à.d. d'une part les conditions physiques du Monde qui monte avec nous, — et d'autre part les conditions physiques (marquées dans l'Eglise) de l'Incarnation qui nous soutient. — Une vraie Mystique "de la Matière" exige que nous soyons "ultra"-humains et "ultra"-chrétiens : elle nous force logiquement à être suprêmement réalistes, et suprêmement attachés aux conditions historiques et vitales du développt chrétien. — Et, à cette clef, elle porte en elle-même ses régulateurs, — pourvu que nous lui soyons fidèles jusqu'au bout. —

Mon voyage a commencé normalement. Physiquement, je suis maintenant très bien. La traversée m'a déjà réussi à l'Atlantique. — Trop d'agitation seulement. Trouverai-je seulement les loisirs de penser en arrivant en Chine ?.. C'est le moment de s'abandonner aux événements, — à la "grande communion". — Je m'embarque le 5 août, — ce qui me mettra à Peking vers la fin d'août.

Fidèlement. — et merci

P. Teilhard

Part of a letter by Teilhard de Chardin

*Noosphere* (or thinking sphere) which is co-extensively (but how much more bound together and homogeneous!) super-imposed on the Biosphere.*

The present and the following chapter will be entirely devoted to the study of the development and properties of this new unit of planetary dimensions. The thesis proposed at the beginning (and which is justified in the course of the work) is that if the process of socialisation (as proved by its "psycho-genic" effects) is simply a superior result of corpusculisation in every case, then the Noosphere—the ultimate and supreme product of the forces of social liaisons in mankind—only assumes its full and definitive meaning on one condition: that it be considered in its global totality as forming one single enormous corpuscle in which the biospheric work of cerebralisation is completed after more than six hundred million years.†

# V

## THE FORMATION OF THE NOOSPHERE

B. *The Socialisation of Compression. Totalisation and Personalisation. Future Directions.*

(. . .)

When, after the repeated failure of our attempts to break the circle hemming us in, it finally becomes evident to our minds that the forces of convergence which besiege us could well be not just a temporary accident but the signs and outlines of a per-manent system in process of establishing itself for ever in the world in which we live, then a really "mortal" fear tends to possess us. In the course of the heralded transformation we are afraid of losing that precious spark of thought lit with such difficulty after millions of years of endeavour—our little "self". It is the essential fear of the reflected element faced by a Whole, which is blind in appearance and whose immense layers are folding back on itself as if to re-absorb it while it still

---

* In fact, to express the true position of Man in the Biosphere, we need a more "natural" classification than that elaborated at present, according to which the human species only appears logically as a wretched marginal ("family") sub-division, although it behaves functionally as a terminal and unique "inflorescence" on the Tree of Life. (Author's note).

† pp. 105-107 (Editor's note).

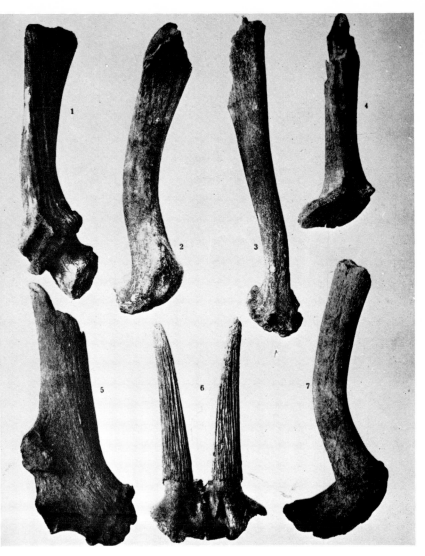

1-4. Cervus megaceros: Antler    6. Gazella prjewalskyi: horns
     stems.                          and frontal bones.
5. Cervus elaphus: antler stem.    7. Cervus megaceros: antler
                                             stem.
Specimens 1-5 and 7 seem to have been broken and shaped by man
for use as tools or tool-handles.

One of the last portraits.

lives. . . . Will we not then have emerged not only in consciousness, but (as Lachelier says) into the consciousness of consciousness, only to sink into an even darker unconsciousness?—as if
after having carried us at arms length towards the light, Life
were to sink back exhausted?

At first sight, this pessimistic and depressing idea of a decline
or senescence of the Spirit due to the general ankylosis of the
human mass is not without some appearance of reality. The
first clearly coercive effects of factory work and the first brutal
and enclosing forms taken by the political formation of states, the
frightening (all the more frightening as it is badly understood)*
example of Ants or Termites—all these impressive symptoms
provide a certain justification for the instinctive gesture of
apprehension and retreat which, before our very eyes, send so
many human beings back towards henceforth obsolete forms of
individualism and nationalism, in the face of the inexorably
increasing totalisation of the Noosphere.

But it is at this very point that it becomes necessary to proceed
scientifically in order to discern the true significance of what is
taking place. What we must do, under the circumstances, is to
replace the particularly critical element of the curve which
marks our life at this moment on as wide a trajectory as possible.
We must see things from a certain distance and a certain height.
Let us therefore return to a view of the Universe in the process
of coiling around itself. Seen from this point of view (which has
never deceived us yet in the course of this enquiry), does it not
immediately become clear that our fears of "dehumanisation
by planetisation" are exaggerated since this planetisation
which frightens us so much is nothing else (judging by its
effects) than the authentic and direct continuation of the
evolutionary process out of which the human zoological species
has emerged historically? Only a moment ago we were remarking that the final result of the physico-social compression to
which we are subjected is to psychically stimulate the human
mass. Well then, once we have understood this, we do not need
any other proofs to be sure that the form of super-grouping
towards which we are being impelled by the movement of

---

* i.e. without taking into account the radical difference between the
"mechanisable" psychism of insects, and the "unanimisable" psychism of
humans. (Author's note.)

F

civilisation is far from representing any one of these material aggregates ("pseudo-complexes") in which elementary liberties neutralise themselves as a result of great numbers or else mechanise themselves by geometric repetition, but instead belongs to the species of "eu-complexes" (cf. Chapter 1) in which the arrangement shows itself *ipso facto* to have a biological nature and value both because of and by virtue of its being a generator of consciousness.*

(. . .)

To maintain the interplay and the tension of the constantly increasing and always fallible sum of all our liberties, a *super-condition* reveals itself—namely that, *pari passu* with the Evolution which reflects on itself, the reasons and the taste for living (i.e. what we have just called "the inner polarisation") become strengthened in the depths of the human soul. This implies the maintenance of a cosmic "atmosphere" around us which becomes always clearer and warmer as we progress forward: clearer because of the foreseen approach of an Outlet through which the most precious of our works can go forward to escape for ever from the menace of total death, warmer because of the increasing radiation of an active unanimous-making hearth. Nothing apparently will be able to prevent the Man-species from still growing (just like Man—the individual—for good . . . or for evil) if he still preserves the passion for growth in his heart. But also there is no exterior pressure, however strong, which could prevent him from going on strike, even given the available amounts of energy, if by misfortune he were to lose interest or faith in the movement calling him forward.

This leads us to formulate the following proposition as a conclusion: "If the pole of psychic convergence towards which Matter gravitates as it arranges itself were nothing other, or nothing more, than the totalised, impersonal and reversible grouping of all the cosmic particles of thought momentarily reflected on each other, then the World would stop coiling in on itself (through disgust with itself) in proportion as Evolution, as it progressed, became more clearly aware of the blind-alley into which it was heading. On pain of being powerless to form the keystone of the vault of the Noosphere, the "Omega" can only be regarded as being the *meeting-point* between the

* pp. 134-7 (Editor's note).

Universe which has reached the limits of centerisation and *another* still deeper *Centre*—a self-subsisting Centre an absolutely ultimate Principle of irreversibility and personalisation: the only true Omega . . ."

And it is at this point, if I am not mistaken, that the Science of Evolution (so that Evolution may show itself capable of functioning in a hominised milieu) has to reckon with the problem of GOD—the Motor, the Gatherer and onward Consolidator of Evolution.

*Paris, August 4, 1949*.

\* pp. 161, 162 (Editor's note).

Very Reverend Father Janssens
Rome.

*Cape Town, October 12, 1951.*

Very Reverend Father,

**P.C.**

I feel that my departure from Africa (i.e. after two months' work and calm in the field) is a good time to let you know in a few words what I am thinking and where I stand, without forgetting that you are the "General" but at the same time (as in our too short conversation three years ago) with that frankness which is one of the most precious assets of the Society.

1. Above all I feel you must resign yourself to taking me as I am, that is, with the congenital quality (or weakness) which, since my childhood, has resulted in my spiritual life always being completely dominated by a kind of profound "feeling" of the organic reality of the world. This feeling was at first rather vague in my mind and my heart but, with the passing of the years, it has gradually become a precise and overwhelming sense of the Universe's general convergence upon itself—a convergence coinciding with and culminating at its summit in Him in *quo omnia constant*, and whom the Society has taught me to love.

In the consciousness of this progression and synthesis of all things *in Christo Jesu*, I have found an extraordinary and inexhaustible source of clarity and inner strength, and an atmosphere outside which it is now become physically impossible for me to breathe, to worship, to *believe*. And what may have been taken in my attitude during the last thirty years as obstinancy or insubordination is simply the result of my own inability to contain my sense of wonder.

This, then, is the psychological condition from which everything derives, and which I can no more change than I can my age or the colour of my eyes.

2. This having been said, I can only reassure you about my inner state of mind by insisting on the fact that (whether or not this generally applies to others than myself) the immediate effect of the inner attitude I have just described is to bind me even more firmly to three convictions which are the very essence of Christianity.

The unique value of Man as the spear-head of Life; the position of Catholicism as the axis in the convergent mass of human activities; and lastly, the essential consummating function assumed by the resurrected Christ at the centre and the summit of Creation: these three elements have sent (and continue to send) their roots so deeply and so inextricably into the whole of my intellectual and religious world that it is henceforth impossible for me to tear them out without destroying everything.

Truly (and by virtue of the whole structure of my thought) I feel myself today more indissolubly bound to the hierarchical Church and the Christ of the Gospels than at any other time in my whole life. Never before has Christ seemed to me more real, more personal, or more immense.

How, then, can I believe that the path I am following is an evil one?

3. The fact remains, as I am fully aware, that Rome may have its reasons for esteeming that, in its present form, my view of Christianity is premature or incomplete and that it may be inopportune to diffuse it more widely at the present moment.

It is on this important point of outward loyalty and obedience that I particularly desire (in fact this is the real point of this letter) to assure you that I am determined to remain a "child of obedience" despite any appearances to the contrary.

Obviously I cannot renounce my inner searching without risking an inner catastrophe and disloyalty to my most cherished vocation, but (and this has been the case for some months) I am no longer propagating my ideas and am only trying to obtain a deeper personal understanding of them. This attitude has been made much easier for me by the fact that I am once more able to do first-hand scientific work.

In fact I have every hope that my absence from Europe will allow the controversy about me, which has disturbed you recently, simply to die down. Providence seems to be lending me a helping hand in this direction, for the Wenner-Gren (the ex-Viking) Foundation of New York which sent me here (the same incidentally, which refloated Father Schmidt's *Anthropos* after the war) is already asking me to prolong my stay in America as long as possible, with a view to revising and developing the results of my work here. All this allows me to gain time and gives a purely scientific orientation to the end of my career . . and my life.

In my opinion—let me say it again—these lines are a simple avowal of conscience and call for no reply from you. See in them only the proof that you can completely count on me to work for the Kingdom of God, which is the only thing I can see and which interests me, beyond the bounds of Science.

Yours most respectfully *in Xto filius*,

P. Teilhard de Chardin

From: P. Leroy, *Le P. Teilhard de Chardin, tel que je l'ai connu*, Paris, 1958.

# A SUMMARY OF MY PHENOMENOLOGICAL PERSPECTIVE ON THE WORLD

### Point of departure and key to the entire system

"THERE exists a cosmic drift of Matter, propagating itself against the current throughout Entropy, which is moving towards increasingly complicated states of arrangement (in the direction—or in the interior—of a 'third infinite' the *Infinite of Complexification* which is as real as the Infinitely Small or the Immense). And consciousness reveals itself experimentally as the result, or *specific* property of this Complexification taken to extreme degrees."

If this law of recurrence (known as "of complexity-consciousness") is applied to the history of the World, a rising series of critical points and singular developments will appear as follows:

1. *Critical point of vitalisation.*

Somewhere, on the level of Proteins, an initial emergence of Consciousness takes place in the heart of the Pre-living (at least for our experiment). And thanks to the concomitant mechanism of "reproduction", the rise of Complexity is accelerated on Earth by means of the *phyletic way* (genesis of species or *speciation*).

From this stage (and in the case of higher forms of living beings) it becomes possible to "measure" the progress of organic Complexification by the progress of cerebration. Thanks to this device, a privileged axis of Complexity-Consciousness—that of the Primates—can be perceived in the heart of the biosphere.

2. *Critical point of reflection* (or Hominisation).

As a result of some "hominising" cerebral mutation taking place among the Anthropoids towards the end of the Tertiary period, psychic Reflection, which is not only *knowing* but *knowing that one knows*, makes its irruption into the World and opens an entirely new domain to Evolution. In man, under the appearances of a new simple zoological family, *a second species of life* is in fact developing, with its new cycle of possible arrangements and its own special planetary envelope (the Noosphere).

3. *Development of Co-Reflection* (and rise of an ultra-human).

When applied to the great phenomenon of human Socialisation, the criterion of Complexity-Consciousness gives decisive indications. On one hand, in human society, an irresistible and irreversible technico-cultural arrangement of noospheric dimensions is manifestly in progress. And, on another hand, as a result of co-reflection, the human spirit is ceaselessly raising itself in collectivity (thanks to the liaisons furnished by technology) to the point of being able to perceive new dimensions: as, for example, the evolutionary organicity and corpuscular structure of the Universe. It is here that the joint process of "organisation-interiorisation" clearly makes its reappearance. In other words, the fundamental process of Cosmogenesis continues as before, before our very eyes (or even starts again with added vigour).*

Considered in its zoological totality, Humanity presents the unique spectacle of a phylum which is making an organico-psychic synthesis with itself. Truly a "corpusculisation" and a "centration" (or centering) of the Noosphere on itself *as a whole* [in English in the original text—Transl.].

4. *Probability of a critical point of Ultra-reflection in the future.*

If we extrapolate it in the future, the technico-socio-mental convergence of Humanity upon itself obliges us to foresee a paroxysm of Co-reflection, at a certain finite distance from us in Time: this paroxysm cannot be better (or otherwise) defined than as a critical point of Ultra-Reflection. Naturally we are unable to imagine or describe such a phenomenon (which apparently implies an escape beyond the bounds of Space and Time). However, certain precise energising conditions which must be

---

* The only difference being that starting with Man, quite clearly, cosmic complexification takes the form not only of a fortuitous arrangement due to large numbers, but ultimately, in its most living parts, of a gradual *self-arrangement* [in English—Transl.] (Author's note).

satisfied by the foreseen event (growing activation, with its approach, of man's "taste for evolution" and his "wish to live") oblige us to conclude that it coincides with a definitive access to the irreversible (since the perspective of total death would bring the process of Hominisation to a dead halt through discouragement).

It is to this superior stage of Co-reflection (i.e. unanimisation, in fact) that I have given the name of "Omega Point" to denote the personalising cosmic cradle of unification and union.

5. *Likelihood of a reaction* (or "reflection") *of the Omega on the Human in the course of Co-reflection* (Christian Revelation and Phenomenon).

The more we reflect on the necessity for an Omega Point to support and inspire the continuation of hominised Evolution, the more we will perceive two things:

First, that a purely conjectural (purely "calculated") Omega Point would be too weak to maintain in the heart of Man a sufficient passion for him to go on hominising himself to the very end.

Second, if Omega Point really exists, it is difficult to imagine that its supreme "Ego" will not make itself directly felt as such in some way to all the inchoate (i.e. all the reflected elements) "ego" of the Universe.

Seen from this point of view, the old and traditional idea of "Revelation" reappears and reintroduces itself (this time by means of biology and evolutionary energetics) in Cosmogenesis.

Seen also from this point of view, the Christian Mystic Current takes on extraordinary meaning and actuality. For if it be true that energising necessities make it absolutely vital for the process of complexity-consciousness to feel the heat of some intense faith in order to complete itself, then it is equally true (it is self-evident once one has taken the trouble to make a general survey of the situation) that no faith is actually in sight which is capable of fully assuming (by amorising) a Cosmogenesis of convergence, except that in a "pleromising" and "parousiac" Christ *in quo omnia constant*.

*New York, January 14, 1954.*

(*Les Études philosophiques*, October-November 1955, new series, 10th year, No. 4.)

# Bibliography

---

## I. WORKS BY TEILHARD DE CHARDIN

### In French

1. Published by Éditions du Seuil, Paris:
   *Œuvres de Pierre Teilhard de Chardin.*
   Vol. 1: *Le Phénomene humain*, 1955.
   Vol. 2: *L'Apparition de l'Homme*, 1956.
   Vol. 3: *La Vision du Passé*, 1957.
   Vol. 4: *Le Milieu divin*, 1957.
   Vol. 5: *L'Avenir de l'Homme*, 1959.
2. Published by Éditions Albin Michel, Paris:
   *Le Groupe zoologique humain*, 1956.
3. Published by Grasset, Paris:
   *Lettres de voyage*, 1956.
   *Nouvelles lettres de voyage*, 1957.

### In English

*The Phenomenon of Man*, Collins, 1959.
*Le Milieu divin*, Collins, 1960.
*The Future of Man*, Collins, 1964.
*Letters from a Traveller*, Collins, 1965.

## II. WORKS ON TEILHARD DE CHARDIN

François-Albert Viallet: *L'univers personnel de Teilhard de Chardin*, Amiot-Dumont, 1955.
Claude Tresmontant: *Introduction à la pensée de Teilhard de Chardin*, Le Seuil, 1956.

Nicolas Corte: *La Vie et l'Ame de Teilhard de Chardin*, Fayard, 1957.

R. P. Leroy, S.J.: *Pierre Teilhard de Chardin tel que je l'ai connu*, Plon, 1958.

Olivier A. Rabut: *Dialogue avec Teilhard de Chardin*, Éd. du Cerf, 1958.

Paul Chauchard: *L'être humain selon Teilhard de Chardin*, Gabalda, 1959.

Paul-Bernard Grenet: *Pierre Teilhard de Chardin ou le Philosophe malgré lui*, Beauchesne, 1960.

N. M. Wildiers: *Teilhard de Chardin*, Éd. Universitaire, 1961.

The most complete work on Teilhard's life, personality, and work is:

*Pierre Teilhard de Chardin, les grandes étapes de son évolution*, Plon, Paris, 1958, by C. Cuénot.

This is the fundamental book for any study of Teilhard de Chardin. One of its many qualities is that it contains a very large selection of texts from Teilhard's own correspondence. Its bibliography is of outstanding value to the student and research worker.

# Index